DATE DUE

MR 5 63			
FE 10 70			
~~Received~~			
~~Curve~~			
DLS			
3/22/94			
MAR 1 8 RECD			
APR 2 8 1994			
APR 2 5 RECD '94			
GAYLORD			PRINTED IN U.S.A

The Biology of Art

The Biology of Art

A STUDY OF THE PICTURE-MAKING
BEHAVIOUR OF THE GREAT APES AND
ITS RELATIONSHIP TO HUMAN ART

by Desmond Morris

NEW YORK
ALFRED A. KNOPF
1962

Contents

CONTENTS

6

CONTENTS

7

Illustrations

FIGURES

9

MONOCHROME PLATES

ILLUSTRATIONS

COLOUR PLATES

Introduction

The news that an exhibition of Chimpanzee Paintings was being held in a London Art Gallery came as something of a surprise to the art world. When it became clear that the pictures in question were not portraits of apes, but were in fact paintings produced *by* chimpanzees, the scientific world joined with the art world in keeping a careful eye on proceedings and in adopting a mildly amused scepticism.

But the experts were not alone. The average Englishman loves animals and hates abstract art. It is not surprising therefore that an animal which paints abstract pictures produces a rather irritating mental conflict. Should one praise the animal or curse the pictures?

The Press, along with many of the visitors to the exhibition, took one extremist view or the other. The pictures were either viciously attacked as an insult to human dignity, or wildly praised as heralding a vital new art form. A few discerning eyes saw them for what they were – a series of unique documents, records of a new and biological approach to art.

In the past, the origins of human art have been probed from several directions – the prehistoric remnants, the folk art of primitive peoples, the pictures of the mentally unbalanced, and the scribbles of children. These sources of information have been valuable in various ways, but each has its own particular shortcomings and pitfalls. The prehistoric, for instance, emerges as a rather sophisticated and advanced level of aesthetic production. The folk art of contemporary so-called primitives is also highly developed and it soon becomes clear that, if there is one thing that can be firmly established about 'primitive art', it is that it is anything but primitive. The art of the insane, a fascinating enough study in its own right, emerges on close scrutiny as a far more specialized field than is sometimes casually claimed for it. Finally, that most promising of sources, the infant scribble, can give a great deal of information about the fundamentals of artistic creation, but quickly runs into trouble as soon as proud parents start peering and coaxing or, worse, scoffing. This happens all too soon and it does great credit to the machinery of the infant brain that, despite this interference, all is not immediately lost.

Surveying this field it is obvious enough that any new source of really *simple* aesthetic material must be invaluable to art theory. This is exactly what the ape picture-makers provide. They show composition control, but a minimum of it; they show calligraphic development, but a minimum of it; they show aesthetic variation, but again at a minimal level. Here, more vividly than anywhere else, it is possible to come face to face with the basic fundamentals of aesthetic creativity.

It is particularly valuable to compare their work with the human infant scribbles and to ask questions about the way in which the two sets of pictures, so similar at the outset, diverge as the two groups of artists grow older, with man rapidly outstripping his hairy cousins.

The aim of this book is to gather together for the first time and analyse all the known information concerning this new biological source of material and then (in the final chapter) to re-examine briefly the development of human art in an attempt to establish a set of biological principles of aesthetics.

1. The History of Ape Picture-Making

If, as I have claimed, ape picture-making provides us with an important new source of material for the analysis of human art, then it is a fair question to ask why this source has been studied so little in the past. To understand this, it is first necessary to look back at the formation of the earliest captive ape colonies.

It was at the turn of the century that a young Harvard student called Robert Yerkes first conceived the idea of setting up a breeding colony of apes for the purpose of making comparisons between the psychology of man and his nearest living relatives. But apes are expensive to obtain, expensive to house, and expensive to feed, and it was not until thirty years later, after numerous vicissitudes, that Yerkes was able to stand and admire the newly completed Orange Park Research Station for Primate Studies, in its sub-tropical Florida setting.

During the thirty years which his plan took to come to fruition, chimpanzee studies were beginning in earnest in several other countries. Apes had, of course, been kept in zoos and circuses for many years, but the earliest important use of these animals for scientific research was by Metchnikoff, in France, in the first years of this century, as a stand-in for man in various medical projects. The details of Metchnikoff's success with these animals influenced Yerkes considerably and at the same time he was able to gain a great deal of practical knowledge from the Abreu primate collection in Cuba, where Mrs Rosalia Abreu had built up an astonishing colony of pet monkeys and apes.

Yerkes was thus spurred on towards this ambitious plan for a full-scale primate laboratory, but was overtaken by the German investigator Wolfgang Köhler who, at a small research station in the Canary Islands, established in 1912, began to make chimpanzee studies of the kind Yerkes was planning for his major station in the United States.

Had it not been for the First World War, the Canary Islands colony would almost certainly have developed and expanded to overshadow the Yerkes project. Köhler's experiments were tremendously successful, but after the war was over the colony was broken up and the chimpanzees sent away to Germany.

Once again, Yerkes was strengthened in his conviction that ape studies were of vital importance to biology and, in the 1920's, there was now no captive colony of these animals in existence for purely scientific research purposes. After years of delays and frustrations, Yerkes finally achieved his goal in 1929 and building of the new station was completed in 1930.

Pre-war Investigations

It was the establishment of this colony that led directly to one of the first published reports of primate picture-making. In 1931, a seven-and-a-half-month-old female chimpanzee called Gua was separated from her mother. The young ape had actually been born in captivity in the Abreu colony in Cuba, but the latter was disbanded in 1930, owing to the death of Mrs Abreu. Thirteen of the chimpanzees, including Gua and her mother, were transferred to the newly opened Florida station.

Gua was loaned for a period of nine months to a young professor of psychology, W. N. Kellogg, and his wife, at Indiana University. The Kelloggs had a son ten months old and the boy and the ape lived together as companions during the experimental period. The results of this study were published in 1933. (*The Ape and the Child* by W. N. and L. A. Kellogg.)

Day by day, during the nine months the ape spent with them, the Kelloggs tested, observed and examined every conceivable similarity and difference between the two infants. One of the many tests was drawing on paper with a pencil. There was no special attention focused on this particular test by the experimenters either before or after the results were obtained. The discovery that the chimp, like the child, would scribble if given the chance, did not apparently make any great impact on the Kelloggs, as they report the results of the tests extremely briefly. This is not surprising, however, since the wealth of new information emerging daily from their study must, at that date, have been overwhelming.

The scribbling of the chimpanzee resulted from the fact that each

16

month Gua and the Kelloggs' son Donald were both given the 'Gesell Tests for Pre-school Children'. This test series comprises approximately 150 carefully standardized experiments of a very simple nature that can be carried out with infants to establish whether they are advanced or 'backward' children.

In the case of Donald and Gua they were applied to ascertain the relationship between the development rates of the two species. By the fifth monthly testing, when Gua was twelve months and Donald was fourteen and a half months old, a response to the so-called 'Gesell writing test' was obtained for the first time in both. To score in this test the infant simply has to make scribble marks of any sort when offered a pencil and paper. The Kelloggs (p. 263) reported that 'Gua does this excellently after a brief demonstration by the examiner, but Donald does it for the first time *spontaneously*, that is, without any demonstration whatever'.

At the next, the sixth, monthly testing Gua performed the scribbling test spontaneously also, catching up, in this respect at least, with the human infant. She fell behind Donald again at the eighth testing, however, when (p. 266) 'Donald proves superior . . . in drawing a straight line in imitation of the examiner, instead of simply scribbling'.

These are the only observations made on Gua's scribbling responses, except for the following description of a 'play' pattern seen when Gua was thirteen and a half months old:

Probably one of the most astonishing and genuinely childlike forms of non-social or self-play in which Gua ever indulged, was to occupy herself with the moisture of her breath which had condensed upon the window pane. She would make marks in the fogged area with the nail of her index finger and also with the end of the finger itself. Of course her tracings had no particular direction or shape; yet the very fact that she would draw them in this fashion was in itself, it seemed to us, an unusually high type of behaviour, comparable probably to early scribbling in children. It cannot be said that she deliberately blew her breath upon the pane for the 'purpose' of making marks, as our observations suggested that the presence of the mist there was incidental to her previous looking through the window. The well-developed tendency to point her finger at new or strange objects no doubt predisposed her to this kind of reaction. (P. 125.)

To sum up, the Kelloggs made three important discoveries: (1) that a chimpanzee will scribble if shown what to do; (2) that scribbling then becomes a spontaneous action and (3) that the child's scribbles quickly become imitative, but the chimpanzee's do not.

Whilst the Kelloggs were making their ape-child comparison in Indiana, another young female chimpanzee, called Alpha, was also being given the Gesell tests at the Yerkes station in Florida. She received the last of these tests at the age of ten months and at that time had not yet given the drawing response. If Jacobsen, Jacobsen and Yoshioka, who were studying Alpha's reactions at the time, had only carried on for another few months, they too might have reached the vital stage and obtained scribbles from Alpha, as did the Kelloggs from Gua. In retrospect, this seems particularly likely since it was Alpha with whom the first really important and detailed drawing experiments were carried out many years later by Paul Schiller.

The results of the Alpha tests were not to be published until 1951, but, before moving to this post-war period, there are three other early studies that should be mentioned. Firstly, it appears that Alexander Sokolowsky, in the late 1920's, in Germany, had made the basic observation that chimpanzees will draw, since a book of his called *Erlebnisse mit wilden Tieren* (1928) contains a reproduction of a drawing by a chimpanzee called Tarzan II from the Hagenbeck Zoo.

Secondly, H. Kluver, in his book on *Behaviour Mechanisms in Monkeys* (1933), mentions that a capuchin monkey of his drew lines on the floor with coloured chalks. This is the earliest record of picture-making by a monkey, as opposed to one of the great apes, and it is particularly interesting that in the other two instances of sub-ape picture-making the monkey species involved is the same. Kluver's main interest in the drawings was to see if the capuchin would copy a line or figure shown to it. In this respect, he was disappointed.

Thirdly, there was an important study made in Russia. It is not known exactly where the original influences came from to initiate this investigation in Moscow; possibly from Metchnikoff in France, or Kohler in the Canary Islands, or perhaps the interest in the field arose quite independently. Whichever happened, it is known that, in 1913, Mrs Nadie Kohts (Plate

One) began a detailed study which paralleled in many ways the Kelloggs' later child-ape investigation. Despite its early start, however, the Kohts report was not published until 1935, two years after the Kelloggs' book had appeared.

The similarity of the two studies can be judged from their titles. The Kelloggs', as mentioned earlier, was called *The Ape and the Child*, whilst the Kohts document had the title *Infant Ape and Human Child*. The Kohts volume includes photographs of chimpanzee scribbles and compares them with those of the child. These Russian ape drawings must have been executed before 1916 and are therefore the earliest ones known.

The Kohts study differs in one important respect from that of the Kelloggs. The latter studied their chimp and child simultaneously for nine months, whereas Kohts studied her chimpanzee for three years, from 1913 to 1916, and her child for four years, from 1925 to 1929. Comparisons by Kohts are therefore being made between responses separated in time by a minimum of twelve years. However, one or two points of fundamental importance are made in connection with differences in the development of the drawings of the two species.

Kohts shows four pictures (see Fig. 1), two by Roody, her young son, and two by Joni, the infant chimpanzee. In each case there is a 'first-stage' and a 'second-stage' drawing. The two early drawings comprise simple line-scribbles and are identical in style. The two later pictures, however, are completely different, both from the early ones and from one another. Kohts states that 'Notwithstanding Joni's constant fidgeting with a pencil, his accomplishments in the field of pencilwork never went beyond tracing several intersecting lines, while Roody (at 2 or 3) could already master some elementary sketches of surrounding objects'.

There are two significant points made by Kohts here. Firstly, she establishes for the first time that chimpanzee scribbles can change and develop. Joni's early drawing differs considerably from his later one, the simple lines changing to highly characteristic criss-crossing in which bold long lines are crossed with shorter ones, usually at right angles. This later stage of drawing clearly involves a deliberate intersection tendency and is therefore the first recorded example of visual control in ape drawing.

19

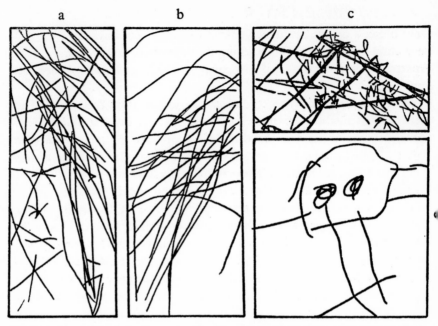

FIG. 1. Four drawings from the Russian study by Kohts showing: (a) Early scribble by chimpanzee Joni. (b) Early scribble by the experimenter's son Roody. (c) Later drawing by Joni showing greater control and with distinct intersection tendency, but no imagery. (d) Later drawing by Roody showing development of recognizable image. (*After Kohts, 1935.*)

Secondly, Kohts notes the all-important difference between the two species by stressing that although there is some sort of development in the chimpanzee scribbles, it does not reach the stage of image-formation, as does the drawing of Roody. Beyond this Kohts does not go, but already it is an important first step.

The Alpha Experiment

Despite the interest of these early studies, they were nevertheless general works which only touched briefly on the picture-making capacities of chimpanzees. It was not until 1951 that the first publication appeared which was specifically concerned with ape drawings.

This came from the Yerkes laboratory but, surprisingly, makes no reference to the observations of either Kohts or the Kelloggs. This does not mean that their influence was entirely absent, however, for the paper, entitled 'Figural preferences in the drawings of a chimpanzee', was not published until after the death of its author, Paul Schiller. Had Schiller lived, the reference list might well have included these earlier studies, but all that was found by Schiller's colleague, K. S. Lashley, amongst the former's effects, were 200 chimpanzee drawings by Alpha and some brief notes.

Luckily Lashley had been close to the work and had even carried out some of the early tests with Alpha himself, so that he was able to compile and edit the Schiller notes into a well-organized report. He was not, of course, able to record all the early influences which led up to the Schiller experiment and quite rightly confined himself to presenting and ordering the results obtained from Alpha.

These results are too detailed to be discussed at length here, in this brief historial sketch, and will be left, for detailed examination, until a later chapter. Briefly, they establish beyond doubt the fact that, in the drawings of a chimpanzee, it is possible to demonstrate not only a change of style over a period of time, as Kohts found, but also a distinct and undeniable sense of design and patterning. Experimental cards with various markings were given to Alpha and she was allowed to draw on them. Repeatedly it was seen that the position and nature of the markings on the cards influenced the way in which the ape scribbled (see Fig. 12).

Schiller established therefore that, not only are the chimpanzee drawings visually organized and controlled, but also that they are capable of experimental manipulation.

The Congo Story

It was in 1953 that, quite by accident, this paper first came to my notice and I determined then and there to continue Schiller's work. At the time I was at Oxford University studying the behaviour of fish, and I soon realized that chimpanzees would not be the easiest of experimental animals to keep and maintain. Three years later I moved to London to take up the post of Head of the Granada Television and Film Unit at the London Zoo.

One of my new duties was to present a weekly animal programme from the zoo and it was suggested that I should develop one particular animal as a programme mascot. This gave me the chance I had been waiting for and without delay a young chimpanzee was obtained and installed at the Television Unit.

It was a one-year-old male and was named Congo. During the first few months its only functions appeared to be biting, eating, screaming and urinating and, despite its growing popularity on television, I was beginning to despair of ever succeeding with any serious experimentation. Unlike Gua, Congo had not been born in captivity. He was approximately one year old in May 1956, when he first arrived at the zoo, and had spent most of his first year as a wild animal in a tropical African forest. Little by little, however, he began to change and soon became more than just a mascot. In November 1956, at approximately one and a half years of age, he produced his first drawing (Fig. 2) and this is how I recorded the incident at the time:

> I held out the pencil. His curiosity led him towards it. Gently I placed his fingers around it and rested the point on the card. Then I let go. As I did so, he moved his arm a little and then stopped. He stared at the card. Something odd was coming out of the end of the pencil. It was Congo's first line. It wandered a short way and then stopped. Would it happen again? Yes, it did, and again, and again. Still staring at the card, Congo began to draw line after line and, as I watched, I noticed that he was beginning to concentrate the lines in one particular region – a part of the card where there was a small ink blot. This meant that, even in this very first scribble, Congo's lines were not just random scratchings and like Alpha, he carried in him the germ, no matter how primitive, of visual patterning. (*The Story of Congo*, p. 61.)

From that point on, Congo produced picture after picture and it was soon clear, even from his earliest scribbles, that his drawings were going to be susceptible to experimental manipulation. But experimental drawings with specially marked papers were not attempted in 1956. It was felt that it was essential for the relationship between the experimenter and the ape to be established and strengthened to the point where there was a perfect rapport, a complete mutual trust and understanding. Unfortu-

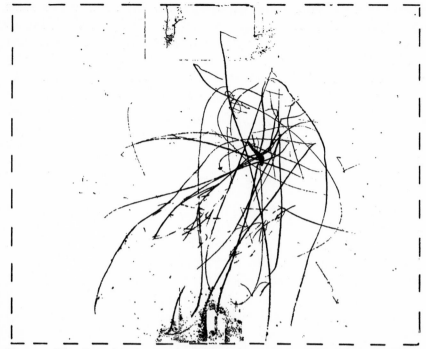

FIG. 2. The first drawing made by the chimpanzee Congo at the London Zoo. Note the orientation of the lines in relation to the position of the accidental blot.

nately, many experiments with chimpanzees in the past have lacked this vital development, with the outcome that the results obtained are clouded by chimpanzee temperament and personality factors and other interference elements that creep in if these highly sensitive creatures are treated like other, more simple, experimental animals. (A zoologist once complained to me that he had spent three whole days working on a test with a chimpanzee, but could not obtain any significant results. Had it been three years instead of three days, I would perhaps have had some sympathy for him.)

Just as I was ready to start serious experimental drawing tests with Congo, a new ape picture-maker appeared on the horizon. Her name was

23

Baltimore Betsy (Plate 2) and she was establishing a new and dramatic approach to the subject, in the form of finger-paintings (Plates 3 and 4). These paintings had won her a great deal of publicity and their arrival on the scene at that time was to interrupt my quiet experimenting in a way which I shall describe in a moment. But first, what of Betsy and her background?

The American Finger-painters

Finger-painting has been employed by child psychiatrists as a technique for self-expression in human infants for many years. It was undoubtedly these studies that first suggested the use of this simple method with the chimpanzees. The earliest record of chimpanzee finger-paintings is in 1953, when three young apes called Christine, Beth and Dr Tom, were all hard at work in the United States.

Christine lived on a farm in Pennsylvania with her owner Lilo Hess, the animal photographer. The young chimpanzee was only six months old when obtained and was the subject of a photographic study by Hess for several years. At the age of two, Christine was given a blackboard and some chalk and began drawing straight away. Unfortunately she ate all the chalk but, in the words of Lilo Hess:

> When I got some more the next day, I kept a close watch on her when she drew. Her drawings consisted of irregular lines and circles similar to those of a young child. She liked to do it, but never stuck to it for very long. It was different with finger-painting. She liked this best of all. The colours intrigued her, though I doubt that she used them with any feeling for their combination. She liked the texture of the paints and enjoyed squeezing them through her fingers. As soon as she saw the box of paints she said, 'Ahh-ahh', for 'Very good', and jumped excitedly up and down. She would play with the paints for as long as I let her. Her designs are so similar to a human child's that a psychologist could not tell them apart. (*Christine*, p. 31.)

Over at the Baltimore Zoo, Beth* and Dr Tom were about to prove this last point. These two young chimpanzees were a one-year-old female and a three-year-old male respectively and they appeared each week on a local TV programme called 'This is Your Zoo'. Arthur Watson, the zoo's

* Apparently an earlier name for Betsy.

PLATE 1. Nadjejeta Kohts and her young chimpanzee Joni in Moscow in 1913. This is the earliest known example of infra-human picture making.

PLATE 2. Baltimore Betsy in action, producing a finger-painting.

PLATE 4. Finger-painting by chimpanzee Betsy.

PLATE 3. Finger-painting by chimpanzee Betsy.

PLATE 5. Congo in action, producing a brush-painting.

PLATE 6. Brush-painting by Congo, showing typical radiating fan pattern. (*Collection Mrs G. L. Carrow, London.*)

PLATE 7. Sophie, an adult gorilla at the Rotterdam Zoo, concentrating on a drawing.

PLATE 8. Well-formed fan drawn on the wall of his cage by capuchin monkey Pablo.

PLATE 9. Sophie producing a painting watched by her keeper, Baris.

director, provided finger-painting equipment for the chimps as an item on one of these programmes and the results were so fascinating that it started him off on a long series of finger-painting sessions, culminating in the spreading abroad of Betsy's fame in 1957. During this period the Baltimore apes' finger-paintings were proving rewarding to the zoo as well as to the chimpanzees and were being sold in large numbers.

In 1954 Baltimore finger-paintings were shown to child psychologists, who boldly identified and analysed them. One of Dr Tom's pictures, the psychologists decided, was by an aggressive seven- or eight-year-old boy with paranoid tendencies. Beth's work was interpreted as that of a fiercely belligerent ten-year-old girl of the schizoid type. A second picture by Beth was also identified as by a ten-year-old girl, but in this case it was said to be of the paranoid type and was reputed to show a strong father identification.

It is easy to laugh at these interpretations, but in fairness to the psychologists concerned, it should be stressed that the conclusions drawn were based on years of study of thousands of finger-paintings by *human* children and, unless the material provided in a scientific test is of the same class as that used initially, little significance can be placed on the judgements, one way or the other. The important fact here, however, is that the child psychologists concerned, used as they were to studying thousands of human infant pictures, were not able to distinguish the ape pictures as infra-human. This is probably the only valid point that can be made in this case, although it is worth remembering that the psychologists did identify the sexes correctly, that the muscular age of a chimp is well in advance of that of a child, and finally that, after appearing on television each week, aberrant mental tendencies are not so unlikely, even in a chimpanzee.

Unfortunately, the commercial success of the Baltimore pictures prevented the development of any serious experimental work. Since the project was also accompanied by wide publicity which inevitably could not resist the all-too-obvious opportunity to deflate some of the pomposities of the art world, it is small wonder if the subject was treated as little more than a zoological joke.

The Trans-Atlantic Challenge

As I said earlier, I was just about to start serious testing with Congo's drawings when the news of Betsy's success filtered across the Atlantic. Congo was not, of course, primarily an experimental animal. His first duty was to his television public and it was soon clear that he was not expected to leave Betsy's position unchallenged. Instead of proceeding to experimental drawings, Congo was switched to painting (Plate 5).

I rejected finger-painting as a technique, however, and developed a method with Congo using brushes (see next chapter). Finger-painting may be pleasing to look at, but this is largely due to accidental texturing, rather than any deliberate patterning by the chimpanzee. Finger-painting is, in fact, of so little value analytically that child psychologists have also recently switched more and more to brush techniques. Alschuler and Hattwick, in their study of *Painting and Personality* in human infants have, for example, rejected finger-painting as a method: 'because of the difficulty of interpreting finished products, inasmuch as first patterns were eradicated by later ones with no trace of the intermediate steps for subsequent analysis'. (*Painting and Personality*, Vol. I, p. 171.) Although brushwork is preferable to finger-painting, this eradication difficulty is not completely eliminated, but only reduced, a brush stroke still being harder to analyse than a pencil mark. Another disadvantage with the paintings was that they involved the use of colours (the reason for this will be explained in the next chapter when methods are being discussed).

Although academically interesting in certain respects, ape paintings are almost always misinterpreted when the finished pictures are shown. But the move over to painting proved to be a mixed blessing, rather than a total loss because, with the more dramatic results produced by this method (see Plate 6) a great deal of attention soon came to be focused on Congo's picture-making abilities and, when experimental work was eventually carried out, the way had been paved for it already.

A special television programme was devoted to Congo's paintings, during which he demonstrated his skill to an audience of 3,000,000. At the end of the programme it had been arranged that I should issue a challenge to any other ape to produce pictures of equal quality. This challenge must have reached Baltimore, for shortly afterwards the director of the London Zoo received a communication from Arthur Watson proposing that twelve Betsy paintings should be sent to London to be exhibited with twelve Congo paintings, and that the exhibition should then go to the United States, where he would exhibit it himself in a similar way.

Arrangements were made accordingly and, in September 1957, a two-chimp show of paintings by Congo and Betsy was held at the Institute of Contemporary Arts in London. The exhibition was opened by Sir Julian Huxley, who stressed the evolutionary aspects of the work. As he later wrote:

The results show conclusively that chimpanzees do have artistic potentialities which can be brought to light by providing suitable opportunities. One of the great mysteries of human evolution is the sudden outburst of art of a very high quality in the Upper Paleolithic period. This becomes more comprehensible if our apelike ancestors had these primitive aesthetic potentialities, to which was later added man's unique capacity for symbol-making.

The exhibition aroused a great deal of interest but it also clouded the issue to some extent. True enough, it had been possible to rush through the first experimental tests, with successful results, in time to include a panel of these at the gallery just before the show opened, but the serious purpose of the investigation was almost obliterated by the joyous reaction of the popular press. Everything from Congo cartoons to Congo calypsos appeared and the situation was rapidly getting out of hand. The Institute of Contemporary Arts was bombarded with requests to put the Congo pictures on sale and, in a weak moment, it was agreed to do so. A rather high price was placed on them, so that only a few would go, to the I.C.A.'s most insistent visitors. A few days later it was decided that this was a mistake and that the selling of the pictures would start a trend that would lead away from the scientific value of the work. To our horror, we found that it was too late, for, in those few days, practically every Congo picture in the exhibition (twenty-four Congos were on show) had been sold.

Luckily a detailed photographic record had been kept of almost all Congo paintings and drawings, but even so, it was decided then and there to put a ban on any further sales at any time.

Congo had painted enough pictures to have a new collection mounted and sent to the United States with the returning Betsy paintings as promised. He had reached a peak of picture-making activity and during the winter of 1957–8 was hard at work completing many series of experimental drawings and also further paintings.

The Other Great Apes

Towards the end of 1957, the first paintings were obtained from an orang-utan, called Alexander, at the London Zoo. The orang showed only mild interest in the proceedings and, although the results (Plates A and B) differed interestingly from Congo's, no further studies were made with this species. Alexander was approximately six years old at the time. If much younger, more active, orang-utans had been available it might have been worth while pursuing this development and perhaps in the future this will be possible.

At about this time, but unknown to me, the third and greatest of the great apes, the gorilla, was being added to the list of painting primates. A particularly docile ten-year-old female gorilla called Sophie had started painting and drawing at the Rotterdam Zoo, under the watchful eye of her keeper, Chris Baris (Plates 7 and 9). Although Sophie was the first gorilla to paint successfully, she was not the first member of her species to be tested in this way. In 1953, Professor Hediger, who was then director of the Basle Zoo, published a report on a successful operation performed on a gorilla at Basle to remove a pencil from its stomach! This dramatic occasion was the outcome of Hediger's pioneer attempt to produce the first gorilla pictures, but although Achilla, the animal in question, did make one or two markings with the pencil before swallowing it, the first and real achievement with this species had to await the study with a controllable specimen such as Sophie.

It was not until 1959 that Sophie's activities came to light when, ironically, she was sent to Basle Zoo for a mating with their male Stefi, who was now successfully paired with Achilla, the latter having fully recovered from her operation. During Sophie's visit, the two females had to take it in turns to live with the male and during her off-duty times Sophie is reputed to have pined for Stefi. It was during these periods that Baris obtained a number of new pictures from her.

Later, back at Rotterdam Zoo, Sophie produced a special series of twelve drawings and paintings at my request (see Plates 10 and 11), and eventually Baris was even able to present her with a test series of experimental papers, which I sent to him, identical to the ones employed in the Congo experiments (see Figs. 32, 33, and 34). The results obtained with Sophie are of particular interest and will be discussed at some length in the chapters dealing with Composition and Calligraphy.

American Brush Painters

During 1957 and 1958 news of further ape picture-makers filtered through from several sources. The Betsy-Congo exhibitions had received widespread publicity throughout the world and a number of other chimps were now being hustled on to the aesthetic band-wagon. Few of these were serious attempts.

Two famous American television chimpanzees, J. Fred Muggs and Kokomo, Jnr., were said to be making pictures, the latter, at least, using brushes to do so. A more serious and apparently independent investigation was being made in Washington at this time with a chimpanzee named Zippy.

Zippy was also working with brushes and produced some rather characteristic results, which were exhibited in the Senate House Museum in Kingston, New York, in the autumn of 1957, at the same time as the Betsy-Congo show was being held at the I.C.A. in London. It was later discovered that, by pure coincidence, the two exhibitions had opened on exactly the same day, September 17th. The unusual feature of Zippy's work is that, in all six of her pictures known to me, the basic motif is horizontal (see Plates 12 and 13). Horizontality as a basic motif was rare amongst other primates and was only found as a dominant theme in Zippy, in a few of Alexander's paintings and in Congo's later work.

The European Scene

During the spring of 1958 a film was made demonstrating Congo's painting technique and this was presented at the XVth International Congress of Zoology in London in July. At this conference the existence of three other primate picture-makers came to light – Bella, a chimpanzee in Holland, Pablo, a capuchin monkey in Germany, and Jonny, a large male chimpanzee at the Vienna Zoo. Of the latter, little was known until the publication of a short paper by the experimenter, Hermann Goja, in the Zeitschrift für Tierpsychologie, in 1959.

It appears that Goja had succeeded, in 1957, in inducing two chimpanzees, Jonny and Fanny, and two orang-utans, Elli and Emil, to draw and paint at the Vienna Zoo, but that only one of the four, the male Jonny, responded satisfactorily, enjoyed drawing, and did so repeatedly. Goja reports that when Jonny was drawing with a pencil

> . . . he moved the latter with small rhythmical movements of the fingertips, shifting the cardboard as he went on and filling it, beginning from its middle, with little scrawls. When using coloured chalk or a brush dipped in colour, he painted larger movements, moving his arm at the elbow-joint. He preferred red to other colours.

I have studied two of Jonny's drawings and they are highly characteristic, made up, as Goja says, of short, weak, meandering lines arranged all over the page in apparently random order (see Fig. 3). It is undoubtedly the fingertip control, with no accompanying arm action, that creates this style. It is astonishing the way in which, as more and more primates are added to the picture-making list, so the individual styles become more and more striking – Sophie, with her tight little zigzags, Zippy, with her bold horizontals, Alpha with her corner-marking, Jonny with his tiny scrawls, and so on.

One interesting point about Jonny was that drawing and painting excited him sexually and the 'sexual excitation increased with the zeal of his occupation'. Judging by his photograph, Jonny is a sexually mature male and is probably the only adult male primate that has been induced to

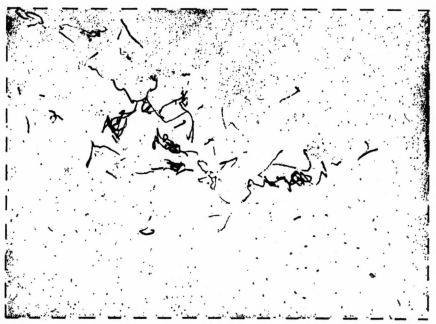

FIG. 3. Typical drawing by adult male chimpanzee Jonny, at the Vienna Zoo.

draw repeatedly (both Alpha and Sophie were adults, it is true, but both were female). Whether this sexual excitement was an aberrant response peculiar to Jonny, or whether it will emerge as a regular accompaniment of drawing when other adult males are tested, remains to be seen. Whichever happens, it is nevertheless a most intriguing observation, worthy of further investigation.

Bella, the chimpanzee in Holland, was studied in the spring of 1958 at the Amsterdam Zoo by Miss Hylkema, under the direction of Dr Antoni Kortlandt.* Kortlandt had been interested for some time in the problem of the ancestry of the Great Apes and was following up all possible

* In 1959 M. Kooy, a second pupil of Kortlandt, obtained thirty pictures from another chimpanzee called Flupje, a two-and-a-half-year-old female. Most of Flupje's pictures were made up of simple straight lines, but one of them showed a moderately well-formed circle.

31

clues concerning any latent ape capacities. In this connexion, he set Miss Hylkema the task of obtaining drawings from Bella, a five-year-old female chimpanzee. This test series was unfortunately cut short and most of the results were lost, but Kortlandt has compiled a brief (unpublished) report, which includes the following passages:

> ... The most striking thing about Bella, when she was in a good drawing mood, was her high level of motivation. Miss Hylkema once made the mistake of interfering when Bella was in the middle of a drawing, with the result that she was bitten by the animal. Bella would never bite when Miss Hylkema interfered with any other activity, not even when taking attractive food away from her. ... Bella was never observed to perform any other activities with the same intense level of concentration, with the exception of social playing and romping. She could even make one drawing after another for a quarter of an hour continuously – an unheard-of degree of perseverance for Bella! ... When she was drawing at full intensity, she took up a lying or crouching position on the ground, completely absorbed and totally uninterested in such things as oranges or sweets until the drawing was 'finished'. ... Gradually the tendency arose to fill the whole sheet instead of only the centre part. After filling the centre, Bella shifted to the as yet blank parts of the paper. When, to her, the picture was finished, she turned the paper over, filled the other side, and then suddenly put the paper in her mouth. ... A tendency to make criss-cross patterns arose at later stages of the experiment, at about the time when Bella showed a stronger urge to fill the whole sheet. ... In all sessions, the interest usually waned after a series of drawings had been completed during a period of from ten to fifteen minutes. Between the successive drawings there was usually a small pause. No further progress was noted after the filling-the-whole-sheet and the criss-cross stage.

What Kortlandt does not mention in his report is that one of the Bella drawings shows a definite fan pattern of the type frequently produced by Congo (Fig. 4). A third example of this fan pattern was seen for the first time at the XVth International Congress of Zoology and arrived from a most unexpected source, namely, a small capuchin monkey named Pablo.

Pablo was being studied by Professor Bernhard Rensch, in Germany, who in 1957 published a report of investigations into the role of aesthetic factors in colour and pattern preference in certain monkeys and apes. He

32

PLATE 10. A drawing by Sophie showing her characteristic short zig-zag style.

PLATE 11. A painting by the gorilla Sophie.

PLATE 12. Painting by the New York chimpanzee Zippy. Note the horizontal motif. (*Collection Mrs E. Crane Chadbourne, Kingston, N.Y.*)

PLATE 13. Painting by chimpanzee Zippy. (*Collection Mrs E. Crane Chadbourne.*)

FIG. 4. Simple fan pattern by female chimpanzee Bella at Amsterdam Zoo.

found that, in certain situations where the animals had to choose between regular and irregular patterns, they preferred the regular or rhythmic patterns. He also made the highly significant discovery that, when aesthetic colour preference tests were repeated after a period of time, some of the animals had changed their preferences, and this Rensch classified as the existence of 'aesthetic vogues' in primates. The importance of this will become clear later when Congo's aesthetic development is dealt with in detail.

In 1958 Rensch published a further report dealing mainly with the extension of the tests to birds and fish. The birds he tested, a jackdaw and a crow, showed preferences for the regular patterns, like the primates. The fish, however, did not. They were more attracted by the irregular

C   33

patterns. At the end of this report, Rensch included a short section on drawings and paintings by primates and published the picture shown here (Plate 8) of the capuchin Pablo drawing with chalk on the wall of its enclosure. This animal is quite clearly caught in the act of producing an excellently formed fan pattern. At the Congress, Rensch compared the symmetry of the fan patterns of Congo and Pablo and cited these as further examples of rhythm or 'regularity preferences' of an aesthetic nature.

The Festival Hall Exhibition

At this point I began to expand my studies of Congo's picture-making. Congo had been producing pictures for nearly two years and during this time had changed his style considerably. It now became possible to compare his graphic development with that of human infants.

In the past, only the brief reference in the Kohts monograph had indicated the possibility of making such a study. But now, with Congo's calligraphic evolution over a two-year period and through several hundred pictures, it was possible for the first time to make detailed comparisons with the already well-tabulated data available from child psychologists.

After discussions with Mervyn Levy, the art critic, it was decided to hold a further exhibition and on this occasion to hang Congo's paintings alongside those of very young children. Levy was also particularly interested in pointing out the relationship between ape paintings and contemporary adult human 'action paintings', and obtained a collection of the latter for the purpose. The three groups of pictures were shown together at an exhibition in September 1958 at the Royal Festival Hall in London.

It was at about this time that Congo himself was beginning to grow out of his painting phase. He was not exactly losing interest. It was rather that his urge to paint was gradually being obliterated by (more physical) competing urges. As a healthy young growing male, he was starting to assert himself and, on those occasions when he was in the mood for 'rhythmic self-expression' preferred to do it with bodily gymnastics, rather than with mere brush strokes. At the end of 1958 we were forced to give full recognition to Congo's impending ape-hood, and he went to live with two young female chimpanzees in the London Zoo's monkey house where, after some months, he has now adjusted to the new living routine.

The 'Six-chimp' Test

During the summer of 1959, I made a special test to investigate individual variation in drawing responses. It was already evident that of the various individual primates scattered from Moscow to New York, which had drawn or painted, there were widely differing styles. But the conditions of the tests were also without doubt extremely varied. It was an open question as to whether a group of chimpanzees, tested one by one, with an identical method and identical materials, would show marked individual

FIG. 5. Drawing by young chimpanzee Josie at the London Zoo. This and the next four drawings were all produced under identical conditions.

35

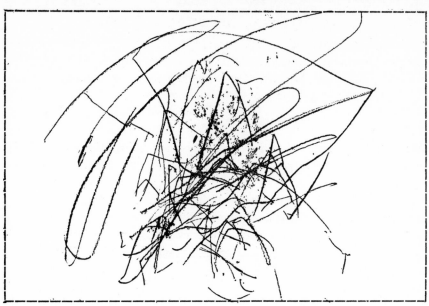

FIG. 6. Drawing by chimpanzee Beebee.

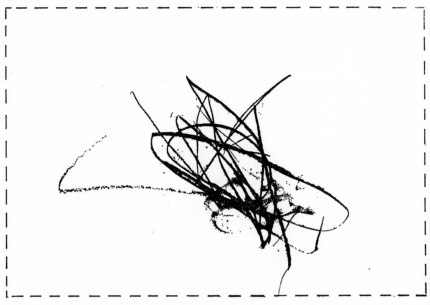

FIG. 7. Drawing by chimpanzee Charlie.

36

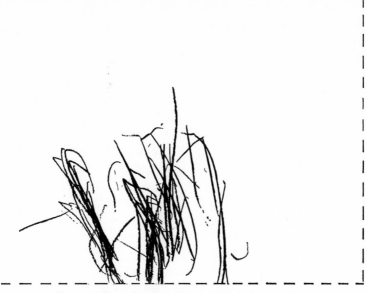

FIG. 8. Drawing by chimpanzee Fifi.

FIG. 9. Drawing by chimpanzee Jubi.

37

differences in the graphic response. It seemed fairly certain because of the very striking range of styles already described, but it was nevertheless worth answering this criticism with a controlled test.

In the new 'Chimpanzee Den' at the London Zoo a group of six chimpanzees live together and are daily put through a series of intelligence tests and exercises for the interest of the public. These animals were ideal material for the experiment because they were fully trained, mentally alert, and had all experienced the same daily routine for some time past. The drawing tests were carried out inside the den and each animal was brought out by itself, tested, returned to the rest quarters, and the next one brought out, until all had been tested. This was done on several occasions and it was quickly discovered that each animal could be identified by its drawing style. Five examples are shown in Figs. 5, 6, 7, 8 and 9. These pictures were drawn under identical conditions on the occasion of the first day's testing, and with equally soft charcoal pencils. Despite this, Beebee's picture, for example, is a soft, gentle, tentative exploration of a new experience, whilst Fifi's is a bold, brash, almost ready-made statement. It is interesting that Fifi was the leader of the group of six and Beebee was a quiet, amiable individual. But this kind of thinking can lead to dangerous mistakes and, until we have many more tests from many more individuals, it will not be safe to make such personality comparisons.

These individual differences were fairly consistent over a number of tests and could not be explained away by age or size differences, although the youngest of the six, a one-year-old male, did refuse to take part in the experiment. Nothing could induce him to put pencil to paper, although he was always re-tested each time.

A particularly interesting point emerged accidentally from this six-chimp test, concerning the way the first line was made by each animal. None had had drawing experience before and I assumed that I would have to go through the same routine that I used on the occasion of Congo's first drawing, with each one in turn. Kortlandt had reported exactly the same need for a preliminary demonstration with Bella's first picture, and there, too, the animal had quickly learned after brief instruction. The Kelloggs had made similar observations with Gua and it may be recalled that they

38

distinguished between ape and child, over this response, stating that Donald showed a spontaneous response, whereas Gua had to be shown a line and how it was made.

This observation cannot, I am afraid, stand up to the facts which the six-chimp test provided. True enough, the first three chimps (Josie, Beebee and Charlie) each had to be shown what to do in the usual way. Also, each one needed no further help after it had made its first line. But then, when the fourth one, Fifi, came out, to my astonishment she grabbed the pencil from me and started to work without any hesitation. The thought struck me that this must be the result of imitation and I turned quickly round to see a dense cluster of young chimps all hanging from the wire of their rest-room at the spot which gave them the clearest view of the drawing Fifi was making. I had been so absorbed in watching the drawings emerge on to the paper, that I had not realized that the Chimpanzee Den was much quieter than usual. I was told afterwards that, behind my back, the silent huddle had hung throughout the tests, intently watching every move, as if their very lives depended on it.

Despite this, the fact that Fifi was the leader of the group made me suspicious. It could just have been that, being the leader, she always took action in a new situation, without waiting for directions. But the fifth chimp, Jubi, answered this doubt. She was small and the least assertive of the group. But, nevertheless, she had seen enough. She did not actually take the pencil from me, but when I handed it to her she straightaway started to draw. When the test was over, I was once again impressed by the tremendous importance that this drawing response can have for apes. Congo several times had screaming tantrums when I had to cut short a session of drawing or painting suddenly. Kortlandt reports similar findings with Bella, Hess found the same with Christine, and here now was this group of young chimps absorbed and fascinated by an activity which they had never experienced before and from which they obtained none of the usual rewards of food that had to be given with their other intelligence tests. Obviously the graphic response is as significant to them as it is to us. One cannot help being surprised, perhaps unreasonably, that the activity is never developed by apes without artificial aid from man.

39

Recent Russian Tests

Lastly, and much to my surprise, word came from Russia late in 1959 that Mrs Kohts was still working with chimpanzees and that, nearly fifty years after she made her first study of chimpanzee behaviour, she and her colleagues in Moscow were obtaining more ape drawings and also drawings from capuchin monkeys.

She very kindly sent me photographs of some of these pictures, a few of which are reproduced here (see Plates 14, 15 and 16 and Figs. 10 and 11). The two capuchins, Claro, a male, and Cobra, a female, were tested in November 1958 (Plates 14, 15 and 16). At the same time, a six-year-old female chimpanzee called Rosa was persuaded to draw for them (Fig. 10). Two adult male chimpanzees also made drawings. One, called Raphael, was

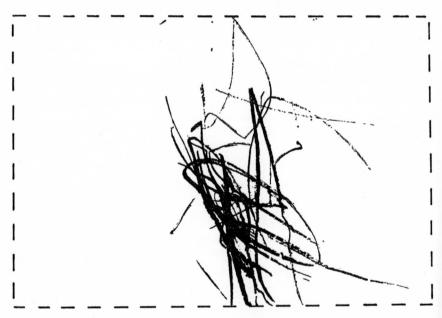

FIG. 10. Drawing by chimpanzee Rosa.

The first orang-utan pictures, by Alexander, a male at the London Zoo. Note the horizontal motif.

Multi-stage paintings, completed in five phases – yellow, red, green, white, and black.

FIG. 11. Drawing by adult chimpanzee Peter, showing central concentrate and corner marking.

tested at the Pavlov Laboratories and the other, called Peter, was from the Moscow Zoopark. Peter's drawings are undoubtedly the most interesting. They show a distinct sense of design with dense masses of scribble concentrated in restricted areas, less condensed scribbling spreading out over the page space, and with distinct corner-marking (see Fig. 11).

This then is the brief history of the twentieth-century phenomenon of 'Ape Art'.

That it should have blossomed at the present time is no accident, for both the worlds of science and art were ripe for it. The former has arrived at a point where, in zoological spheres, objective experimental studies of animal behaviour patterns are flourishing, thanks to the concerted efforts of the comparative ethologists and the animal psychologists. The art world, on the other hand, has experienced wave after wave of increasingly extreme reactions against the fading, traditional, communicatory functions of painting. As a result, human painting today has become increasingly abstract and has returned motivationally to a state similar to that found in the primates, namely pure aesthetic experimentation. With zoology and art in these phases, the stage was set.

HISTORICAL TABLE OF INFRA-HUMAN PICTURE-MAKERS

NAME OF ANIMAL	SPECIES	SEX	AGE IN YEARS WHEN STUDIED	DATE OF STUDY	PLACE OF STUDY	EXPERIMENTER	NO. OF PICTURES
1. Joni	Chimpanzee	♂	1½–4	1913–16	Moscow	Kohts	?
2. Tarzan II	Chimpanzee	♂	?	1928	Hamburg	Sokolowsky	Few
3. Gua	Chimpanzee	♀	½–1½	1931–32	Indiana	Kellogg	Few
4. ?	Capuchin	?	?	1933	?	Kluver	Few
5. Peter	Chimpanzee	♂	Adult	1941	Moscow	Kohts	?
6. Alpha	Chimpanzee	♀	Adult	1941–51	Florida	Schiller	200
7. Achilla	Gorilla	♀	Adult	1952	Basle	Hediger	Few
8. Dr Tom	Chimpanzee	♂	4	1953	Baltimore	Watson	?
9. Betsy	Chimpanzee	♀	1–8	1953–60	Baltimore	Watson	Many
10. Christine	Chimpanzee	♀	2	1954	Pennsylvania	Hess	Few
11. Congo	Chimpanzee	♂	2–4	1956–59	London	Morris	384
12. Alexander	Orang-utan	♂	6	1957	London	Morris	Few
13. Zippy	Chimpanzee	♀	?	1957	Washington	Ecyer	?
14. J. Fred Muggs	Chimpanzee	♂	?	1957	New York	?	Few
15. Kokomo, Jnr.	Chimpanzee	?	?	1957	New York	Garroway	?
16. Sophie	Gorilla	♀	Adult	1957–59	Rotterdam	Baris	Many

43

(*continued overleaf*)

NAME OF ANIMAL	SPECIES	SEX	AGE IN YEARS WHEN STUD-IED	DATE OF STUDY	PLACE OF STUDY	EXPERI-MENTER	NO. OF PIC-TURES
17. Jonny	Chimpanzee	♂	Adult	1957	Vienna	Goja	150
18. Fanny	Chimpanzee	♀	Adult	1957	Vienna	Goja	Few
19. Ellie	Orang-utan	♀	5	1957	Vienna	Goja	Few
20. Emil	Orang-utan	♂	?	1957	Vienna	Goja	Few
21. Pablo	Capuchin	♂	?	1958	Munster	Rensch	Few
22. Bella	Chimpanzee	♀	5	1958	Amsterdam	Kortlandt	Few
23. Claro	Capuchin	♂	?	1958	Moscow	Kohts	?
24. Cobra	Capuchin	♀	?	1958	Moscow	Kohts	?
25. Rosa	Chimpanzee	♀	6	1958	Moscow	Kohts	
26. Raphael	Chimpanzee	♂	Adult	1958	Moscow	Kohts	?
27. Flupje	Chimpanzee	♀	2½	1959	Amsterdam	Kooy	30
28. Fifi	Chimpanzee	♀	4	1959	London	Morris	Few
29. Josie	Chimpanzee	♀	3	1959	London	Morris	Few
30. Charlie	Chimpanzee	♂	3	1959	London	Morris	Few
31. Jubi	Chimpanzee	♀	3	1959	London	Morris	Few
32. Beebee	Chimpanzee	♀	3	1959	London	Morris	Few

44

2. Methods and Materials

Before going on to discuss and analyse the contents of the ape pictures, there are some questions concerning methodology to be answered. It has already been shown that drawing styles can differ from individual to individual, even when standard experimental conditions are applied, but this does not alter the fact that variations in the methods employed to obtain ape pictures will also introduce additional and unwanted variations in the results.

Schiller's work with Alpha was carried out in a standardized manner and Lashley has described this briefly. Also, all the experimental drawings obtained from Congo, Fifi and the other London Zoo chimpanzees were obtained under standardized conditions. Sophie, the Rotterdam gorilla, also used standard Congo test papers for her experimental series.

Of the work of the other primates, little is recorded as to the exact methods used and it is doubtful if, in most cases, any real attempt to standardize the situation was made. In many instances the animals produced so few pictures that the problem can hardly have arisen. The apes were simply given drawing or painting equipment, of whatever kind was to hand, and encouraged to work with it in any way they would. Studies of this type, which have been included in the last chapter in an attempt to give a reasonably comprehensive review, will receive very little attention in the following chapters. Only those tests, the methodology of which can be described here, can justifiably be used when it comes to the question of the analysis of picture contents.

Remote-control Tests

Alpha was a fully adult, eighteen-year-old female chimpanzee when she was receiving her experimental test papers. It was not possible to handle her and all the work had to be carried out with the experimenter outside the animal's cage. Naturally this limited the control to some extent.

45

Before the serious testing had started, Alpha had frequently shown a great interest in scribbling, but no attempt had then been made to standardize the situation:

> When she sees a member of the staff with pencil and notebook, she begs and, if given pencil and paper, retires with them to a corner of her cage. She grasps the pencil with four fingers across the palm and with her thumb extended along it almost to the point. This clumsy grasp makes it necessary for her to keep her forearm almost vertical in order to bring the pencil point on the paper. She places the paper on the floor, makes a few marks on it, usually turns it over repeatedly, and continues to make marks until the pencil point breaks. She uses either hand with equal facility, but more frequently the right.

The main problem for Schiller was to retrieve a drawing from Alpha for analysis. Sometimes she would hand it back, but more often she tore it up. In order to avoid this he constructed a simple frame for use with the test series. This consisted of a 12 in. × 15 in. board, with a short handle, which could be slipped under the cage door and held in position by the experimenter. On the board there was a 2 in. wide grey frame under which the test paper could be fastened. Alpha was thus presented with a drawing area of 8 in. × 11 in., in a set position.

> As test objects, various figures were cut from coloured paper and pasted on to sheets of contrasting colour, or openings were cut in the sheets and contrasting paper pasted behind. Alpha was given one or sometimes two pencils of different colours and allowed to draw for from 10 to 180 secs. before the board was withdrawn. Only rarely did she attempt to snatch the board or to tear off the paper. Throughout the test periods she usually squatted before the drawing board, intent on her scribbling.

There are several disadvantages in this remote-control method. The principal one is that one cannot standardize the position of the ape in relation to the paper. For example, it is reported that 'Alpha usually sat facing the bottom of the figure, but sometimes worked from the side'. This means that, from the study of a completed drawing, the making of which was not witnessed, it would be impossible to distinguish between true vertical and horizontal lines, or between left-right and up-and-down compositional tendencies. Furthermore, if a crossing of lines appeared, it could be a genuine intersection tendency, or simply that the animal made the same type of line before and after a shift in body position. Luckily Schiller made notes at each testing, so that information given about Alpha's various compositional and calligraphic tendencies is reliable enough, but it would be much more satisfactory if the finished products could have been given a top and a bottom, in relation to the position of the animal.

If in the future remote-control proved necessary with certain apes, it should be possible to design a special narrow cage that gave the animal no choice of positions when it approached the drawing board.

Other interesting comments on Alpha's drawing techniques include the intriguing observation that once, when she was starved of paper, she found and tried to draw on a dead leaf. One can hardly resist the fanciful question of what would happen if she was turned loose, with a box of pencils, in her native forests!

Another significant point was her anti-social approach to the subject of picture-making:

> For at least the past ten years her behaviour with pencil and paper has been essentially as at present. During this time she has never been directly rewarded for drawing, and it is quite evident that the activity does not involve social rewards. If possible she retires with her paper to a far side of the cage (in pre-experimental period), turns her back to the observer, works for a time with complete preoccupation, and eventually tears up the paper. If caged with another animal that watches her drawing, she shoulders the other aside or turns away to work in a corner. The motivation is intense. She will disregard food when she sees someone with pencil and paper and will beg for these. The diary records contain frequent notation concerning her interest in mechanical devices and she continually begs for opportunity to untie shoelaces or un-button cuffs. The drive to manipulation is apparently autonomous. A few other of the sixty animals in the colony show similar mechanical interests but in no other adult is it so strongly developed.

It was Schiller's opinion that Alpha was not so much interested in the effects of her drawing as in the action itself. But he has to admit that

> ... there is certainly another factor at work. She does not draw with a pointed stick and discards or chews up the crayon when the point breaks and it no

longer marks. Given paper and pencil with broken point, she retires to a corner, examines the point, makes a few tentative strokes, then returns to the front of the cage to beg. The fact of marking is thus an essential part of the activity.

These last two points, about the nature of the rewards involved in ape picture making, answer two frequent criticisms. The first is that the animal is only scribbling because it is being given food, titbits, etc. When it is explained that no direct reward is given, the next comment is that the animal is nevertheless being rewarded socially by the attentions of the experimenter. The observations with Alpha clearly eliminate that. The other criticism is that the animal may genuinely be getting its reward from doing the drawing, but it is only a reward in the form of the 'motoric pleasure' gained from making the rhythmic arm movements. The fact that Alpha refused to draw with a pointed stick answers that point, and finally leaves no doubt that here is an activity with a visual reward, strictly comparable with the drawing activities of human infants.

Of the other remote-control tests, little can be said. The test with the gorilla Achilla ended in disaster as the animal swallowed the pencil. The tests with the large male chimpanzee Jonny involved the animal 'shifting the cardboard as he went on', so that once again there was no standardization of the test card presentation. Attempts with the little capuchin Pablo, to obtain drawings on removable sheets did not succeed and the only record of the chalk drawings that he made on his enclosure wall is the photograph shown in Plate 8. Clearly, it is preferable to test tame individuals, where the experimenter and the ape sit together, with the latter completely under control, and, if further remote tests are carried out, they should if possible be made in specially designed pieces of apparatus.

Proximity Tests with Congo

All of the 384 pictures obtained from Congo were made whilst the animal was under the age of four and it was therefore possible for the experimenter to work in close proximity with the chimpanzee. For a standard drawing or painting session, Congo was placed into an infant's high chair (see Plate 5). This helped to reduce irrelevant movement and assisted

PLATE 14. Drawing by Moscow capuchin monkey Claro.

PLATE 15. Drawing by Claro.

PLATE 16. Drawing by capuchin Cobra.

PLATE 17. Congo choosing a colour.

PLATE 18. Scratch-lines produced with finger-nails.

in focusing his attention on whatever happened to be placed in front of him on the tray.

As Congo grew larger, it was necessary to modify this tray, a larger board being fixed over it, giving a flat working area in front of the animal of 17 in. × 20 in.

In the case of drawings, a sheet of paper was placed on the board in front of Congo, who was then handed a pencil or crayon and allowed to start work. While he was marking the paper, the experimenter sat immediately in front of him. This position was important as it eliminated any possibility of artificial 'side-effect'. If the experimenter had been sitting to one side of Congo, the latter might have drawn more on that side of the paper simply because he happened to be facing more towards the experimenter.

A single drawing never took more than a few minutes to complete. As with Alpha, it was frequently over in a few seconds. The drawing ended in one of three ways. Either Congo handed the pencil back to the experimenter, or he simply put it down on the board, or alternatively he started to play with it, rolling it about or holding it in his mouth. Whenever any of these things happened, the experimenter held out his hand and waited for Congo to place the pencil in it. When this was done, the drawing was removed and the next paper or card put in its place. After Congo had had a few seconds to scrutinize the new paper (and any pattern there might be on it) he was once again handed the pencil and the whole process was repeated.

A typical drawing session lasted between fifteen and thirty minutes and usually resulted in the production of between five and ten drawings. Sometimes, he was not in the mood for picture-making and lost interest after the first few pictures. At other times he was insatiable and on one memorable occasion worked non-stop for practically an hour, producing the huge total of thirty-three drawings and paintings. But both these very short and very long sessions were rare in occurrence.

It might be argued that strictly controlled timing of the drawings, the pauses and the sessions should have been employed, but the nature of the responses under investigation made this undesirable. Special kinds of tests

D

49

were, of course, made from time to time, but even so these did not usually involve any completely fixed time limit. For example, in some instances Congo was presented with a large number of sheets of paper in quick succession and was only allowed to draw one line on each. The time spent on each of these drawings was naturally less variable, but nevertheless it was the ending of the line that was the finishing-point, not some artificial time limit.

Except in extreme circumstances, no test was ever terminated by the taking away of the pencil, crayon, or brush while the animal was still working with it. In the special tests just mentioned, where he was only allowed to complete one line, even if he wanted to go on, the pencil was not *taken* away. The experimenter simply 'asked for it' by holding out his hand. Performing this action towards Congo became an important 'ritual' in test procedure. During one or two early sessions, before a standard routine had been worked out, attempts to remove equipment that was in use resulted in screaming tantrums, as already mentioned. The fact that Congo, like Alpha, never received any direct reward for picture-making, clearly underlines the powerful character of self-rewarding activities of this type.

There are several difficulties that have to be overcome with a chimanzee, when carrying out tests of the kind described above. Early on, the biting, chewing, or breaking of pencils has to be dealt with. The great apes have extremely muscular lips that are used a great deal to test and investigate any small object, and although Hediger was unhappily powerless to control the gorilla that swallowed the pencil given to it, Congo's early oral investigations of pencils and crayons were easily stopped without any great difficulty by mild threats from the experimenter.

Later, when painting was introduced, the problem re-emerged in the form of paint-sucking. Although non-poisonous water-paints had been carefully selected, the swallowing of any quantity of any kind of paint was undesirable and threats were used once again. They were less effective than before, especially where white paint was concerned. Congo's regular drink at the time was milk and the visual resemblance was such that any attempts to prevent him making oral contact with his 'milk-paint' were met with tantrum outbursts. Happily the problem solved itself with Congo's gradual discovery of the fact that, despite appearances, the 'milk' which materialized during painting sessions was inferior as a food to that which appeared at feeding-time.

As Congo grew older and became more vigorous there was a tendency for drawing or painting sessions to be disrupted from time to time with displays of physical energy. Thumpings, bangings, twistings and balancings in the pauses between paintings sometimes gained such momentum that they interfered with the progress of a session. Apart from normal threat procedure from the experimenter, two additional methods were used to combat this new difficulty. Firstly, Congo was rewarded (with raisins) for sitting still in the chair. Great care was taken that the raisin rewards were not connected directly in any way with the production of paintings or drawings, but only with the cessation of physical exercises. Congo quickly learnt to obey the command 'Sit!' and after a few weeks he no longer required the raisin reward. Secondly, increased facilities for physical exercising were provided immediately before each session.

Under normal conditions only one session was held on any one day and usually only one or two sessions were possible each week. At one period, when the frequency of these tests was greatly increased, Congo soon tired of the proceedings and eventually refused to draw or paint altogether. Even the initial action of placing him in the painting chair produced a screaming tantrum, whereas before it had been the highlight of his day. Schiller had reported a similar experience with Alpha, who at one point was tested intensively for a period of six months, with the result that 'during the last two months it became increasingly difficult to get Alpha to draw and tests were finally terminated because of her loss of interest. When tested again, twenty months after the end of the experiment, she was again very eager to draw'. It was obvious that the only hope with Congo was to rest him completely from picture-making for a while in the hope that he would recover from the surfeit-effect he had experienced. His intensive testing period had only lasted about a week or two, so that it was not felt necessary to rest him for more than a few weeks. This measure proved entirely successful and a few weeks later Congo was desperate to get back to his drawing board. From that point on, however, he was never given more than a few sessions in one week and never more than one a day.

During a typical session, Congo was alone with the experimenter. The presence of more than one human being provided a social situation which tended to distract him. He had grown up with his adopted 'family' without any stunting of his natural social urges and responses. He developed passionate intra-family jealousies and violent inter-family hatreds that could have been suppressed by strict discipline, but which were allowed to continue, within reason, because they were perfectly natural expressions of chimpanzee behaviour. These apes have strong family ties in the wild and also they will not tolerate strangers intruding into their family groups. As he had grown older, there had been an increasing tendency to attack visitors, although his relation with his human 'family' was even more friendly than before. It was getting to the point where, if a visitor wanted to watch Congo at work, the artist was more likely to draw blood than pictures. Luckily, however, several film records of Congo painting had been made at an earlier date.

It was stated previously that each drawing only lasted a few minutes, or less, before Congo lost interest in it. It was also pointed out that if Congo was given a new sheet of paper he would start again with vigour and that in one session a series of five to ten drawings could usually be obtained. This renewed vigour with each sheet of paper was the result of two elements present in the change-over from drawing to drawing. If the ritual of changing over from a completed drawing to a fresh sheet was performed, but with the replacement of the original 'completed' drawing instead of the usual clean paper, Congo would sometimes start off drawing again when he was handed back the pencil. He did this despite the fact that he had previously reached a point where he would not continue with the drawing in question. This was undoubtedly the result of the fact that the period of concentration is extremely short in this species and that the change-over gave a short break and shift in concentration which allowed a re-focusing of interest on the new or replaced sheet of paper. This was not the whole story, however, for Congo was much more likely to re-start on a sheet if it was a genuinely fresh one and not an old one replaced. So the two change-over elements of break-in-concentration and fresh-sheet-of-paper were both important in boosting Congo's drawing vigour.

Although all typical Congo drawings were single-stage products, occasionally multi-stage pictures were obtained in the manner described above. In some of these, where coloured crayons were used, it was only necessary to change the crayon repeatedly for Congo to maintain prolonged interest in the drawing. The paper in these cases was not removed and replaced each time, nor was there any appreciable pause in the proceedings, but simply a change from one colour to another. Each new colour set off a new bout of scribbling and in this way very elaborate drawings could be obtained. However, it is the simplest drawings that are most valuable for analysis at this stage and the majority of Congo's drawings (172 of them) are brief, one-stage, black-and-white, standard-sized (foolscap) pictures.

All the details I have given so far concerning the methods used with Congo applied primarily to the production of drawings, but there were a few special conditions appertaining to the production of paintings. In most respects the problems were the same but one major difference was that, whereas a pencil or a crayon continued to make marks on the paper for some time before becoming blunted, the paint on a brush was quickly used up. As soon as the brush dried up, Congo lost interest and the experimenter had to be ready immediately to exchange it for another which was loaded with paint. In a typical painting session, a brush was placed in each of six pots of (red, yellow, green, blue, black and white) paint. These pots were out of reach of Congo, on a separate table. At the start of a painting he was handed the first brush and allowed to paint until the brush was dry. He was then offered the next loaded brush after having handed back the first one. The first brush was then replaced in its pot and was ready for use again later. Each colour in turn (in a random order) was presented to Congo in this way until he showed signs of losing interest completely, despite the 'boosting effect' of the frequent colour changes. At that point the painting was considered to be finished. It was removed and a new paper was presented and the whole process repeated. In a typical painting

53

session, not more than two or three pictures were forthcoming and frequently only a single one was obtained.

It might be argued that Congo should have been given a free colour choice, allowing him to select from the whole range of six pots each time a brush dried up. Unfortunately there were difficulties involved in this method which reduced its value considerably. On those occasions where it was attempted, Congo was given the six colours in a tray of six dishes (Plate 17). Upon being given a brush he proceeded, each time, to mix the colours together until all the dishes contained a uniform muddy brown. Only then would he show any interest in painting. The mixing was performed with great concentration and sometimes it claimed his attention to the complete elimination of painting on the paper. Possibly, with perseverance, the novelty of mixing could have been reduced to a level where it would have been feasible to give Congo a free colour-choice painting test, but this was not pursued. The main function of the colour variety given to him in normal tests was that of supplying a 'boosting effect', as already described. Congo's slight colour preferences (for reds and oranges) were comparatively weak and of little interest in the present study. Blue appeared to be his least favourite colour, but he seldom refused any colour, as either crayon, pastel, or paint. On rare occasions, when his reactions were at low intensity, he would refuse blue when he was still prepared to work with his favourite reds and oranges. In the case of a typical painting session he was, of course, able to use each colour handed to him as much, or as little, as he liked, so that even with random presentation of colours, one after the other, he was still able to control the colour result to some extent.

As the composition and the calligraphy were the most important aspects of Congo's pictures, greater energy was put into obtaining the simpler black and white drawings, where the exact course and position of each line could be traced and measured. But before painting was abandoned altogether for serious purposes, an attempt was made to improve the clarity of these pictures. This employed a multi-stage process with a set of, say, six sheets of paper of standard size. Congo was given them one at a time and allowed to paint on each one with a single colour, say yellow. Later, when the yellows had dried thoroughly, the sheets were presented again in the same order, but this time a second colour was available, say green. The whole process was then repeated, at intervals, through each of the six basic colours used. The resultant paintings did not then suffer from the accidental merging of colours which automatically took place in the single-stage paintings. The exact patterning, as executed by Congo, was thus more clearly revealed (see Plates C and D).

Several subsidiary techniques were employed by Congo when painting. These were largely accidental in origin. The use of finger-nails for scratching lines in wet painted areas occurred on a few occasions (Plate 18) as did spreading the paint with tongue or fingers. None of these activities was developed by Congo, who showed a certain distaste for becoming soiled with paint. If offered a rag, he cleaned himself carefully. It is well known that chimpanzees do not like water and will avoid getting wet if possible. However, once really wet, they will play with water, or even permit themselves to be bathed. Similarly, if given encouragement to produce finger-paintings, a chimpanzee will at a certain stage overcome the distaste for becoming messy, and when its hands have become thoroughly smeared with paint, will readily proceed to finger-paint at high intensity. (Purely to test this point, Congo was given several finger-painting sessions – see Plates E and F.)

During one particular painting session, Congo urinated on the picture and then proceeded to incorporate the urine into the painting rather in the style of a water-colour wash technique. On several subsequent occasions he obtained the same effect by tipping water over the painting.

If, whilst painting, Congo managed to get hold of objects other than brushes, he would sometimes try them out on the picture in hand. Those which produced the most novel visual effects were preferred. A stiff-bristled plastic hair-brush was used to groom him at one time, just before the painting sessions were begun. Several times he used this, with great intensity, to produce special effects on the painting he was working at (see Plate 19). Once or twice, he used an ordinary paint-brush on its side as a roller, to spread the paint as much as possible.

None of these subsidiary techniques was encouraged as they naturally interfered with any attempt to analyse Congo's basic patterning. They are interesting in themselves though, as indications of Congo's perpetual quest for novelty.

No mention has yet been made of the various grips used by Congo when holding the pencil, crayon, or brush. Either hand was used (Plates 20 and 21) and there did not appear to be any long-term preference for one rather than the other. Short-term differences did appear from time to time, but they seldom persisted through a whole session.

The original grip was a primitive one, with all four fingers held tight round the object, as with Alpha. The thumb was sometimes pointing downwards, with the palm facing outwards (Plate 22), and sometimes it pointed up and the palm was then facing inwards (Plate 23). As Congo grew, so he began to try out new grips until he achieved a sophisticated human-like grip, holding the object between thumb and first finger (Plate 20). Also seen was a grip intermediate between the 'primitive' one and the 'advanced' one (Plate 24). This change in grip was accompanied by an advance in calligraphic variety and it is surprising that it developed without any prompting from the experimenter.

The 'level of intensity' of drawing has been referred to at various points and I must stress that this was not a conclusion arrived at in any particular case simply by noting how rapidly or elaborately the chimpanzee drew or painted. Indeed, some of the most intense picture-making was done rather slowly and deliberately with perhaps quite simple strokes. The level of concentration or intensity was measured by the degree to which other play activities were absent. At the highest intensity, Congo kept his head still and his eyes fixed to the drawing or painting. His body movement was reduced to the arm action of painting or drawing alone. With drawings he sometimes crouched low over the paper, making faint grunting noises as he drew. (These noises were similar to those he made when being tickled under the arms. What the two situations had in common is not clear at present.)

At medium intensities, he kept his body less still and was likely to move his head about or look away at the slightest distraction. At the lowest

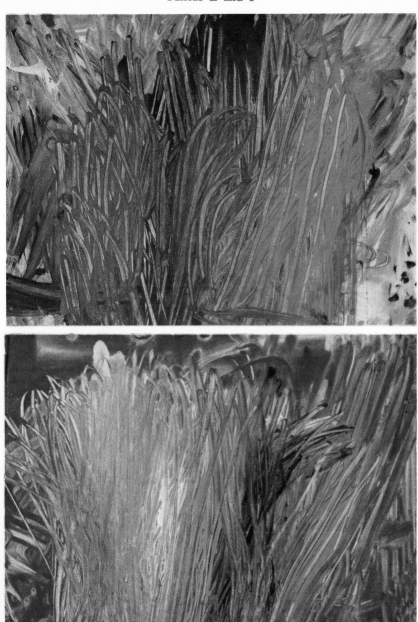

Finger-paintings by Congo.

Lopsided fan pattern. (*Private collection, Los Angeles.*)

intensities, wriggling, banging and arm-waving were interspersed with brief bouts of interest (Plate 25).

If a session had been proceeding for some time and Congo was becoming restless, a point was soon reached when he would refuse to work any longer. He would throw the pencil or brush down as soon as he had been given it, bang the tray and try to crumple up the paper. At that stage there was no hope of prolonging the session any further. To attempt to do so only resulted in a serious tantrum. In fact, as the experimenter came to recognize the signs of waning concentration, so he learned to cut short the sessions before all interest was extinguished, thus reducing the danger of long-term 'staleness'.

Proximity Tests with Other Apes

The tests carried out with Fifi and the other chimpanzees at the London Zoo employed the same methods as those described for Congo, except that I made a short-cut by placing the pencil into their hands in the advanced position on the occasion of their first tests. Some continued to use it with success from that moment on, but others found it strange and experimented until they had achieved the apparently more natural 'primitive' or 'stick' grip, with all four fingers grasped tightly round the pencil.

A photograph in the Kelloggs' book shows that Gua also had this primitive grip, with, in her case, the thumb pointing upwards and the palm facing inwards. She was, like Congo, placed in an infant's high chair and drew on the flat tray in front of her.

Most of the apes seem to prefer working on a flat surface, except Alexander the orang-utan, who would sometimes work away quite happily on a vertical or angled board, but who ignored it when it was placed flat in front of him. Despite this, the few serious tests which were done with him were done on the flat in order to standardize them with the others obtained from the chimpanzees.

The most remarkable photographs of a picture-making ape are undoubtedly those of the enormous Sophie sitting at a table and working so delicately with small, jerky movements at the paper in front of her. The experimental tests she made were done on papers prepared in London, so that her tests were strictly comparable with those of Congo, Fifi, and the other London Zoo chimpanzees. It is worth noting that Sophie has adopted the advanced human-style grip (Plates 7 and 9).

Betsy performed her finger-painting sitting in a chair, at a table, with the paper or board placed flat in front of her. Large blobs of paint were then placed on the board, or on to her hand, and she proceeded to smear these blobs over the surface of the paper, weaving complex patterns with her hands or finger-tips.

These, then, were the methods and techniques used by the various experimenters to obtain the primate pictures. It now remains to analyse their contents.

3. Composition – the Unit Relationships

In the last two chapters we have seen who made the ape pictures, when they were made and how they were made. It now remains to ask *what* was made and this can best be done by separating the picture-contents into their two basic elements: Composition and Calligraphy.

By composition I mean the nature of the spatial relationships between the units of a picture. By calligraphy I mean the nature of each individual unit taken by itself. Composition and calligraphy can, and often do, vary independently of one another and it is possible to discuss composition here at some length before going on to consider calligraphic problems.

THE ALPHA TESTS

It is Alpha who first showed the way to the possibility of a study of visual composition in apes. Schiller noticed that the eighteen-year-old female always restricted her scribbling to the piece of paper she was working on and seldom went off the edge with her markings. Also, she often laboriously marked each corner of the paper before filling in the centre with scribble (Fig. 12a).

He had known for some time that Alpha liked playing with pencils and paper, but this was the first indication that there was any visual organization of the position of the lines in relation to the drawing space. This gave Schiller the idea of presenting sheets of paper to Alpha which were already marked with simple shapes or patterns.

Alpha's tests can be divided into three basic categories: those in which she marked figures, those in which she balanced pictures and those in which she completed patterns. These three tendencies – to mark, to balance and to complete – were present in Alpha to a startling degree, the detailed results being as follows:

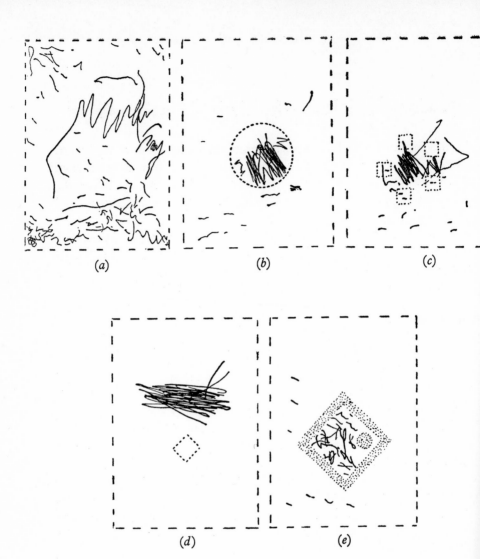

(a)

(b)

(c)

(d)

(e)

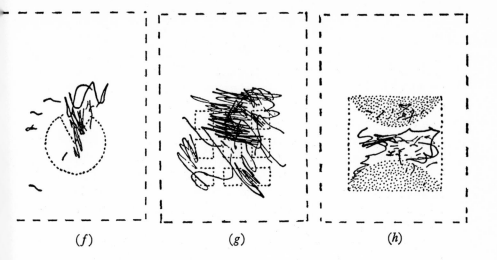

(f)　　　　　　　　(g)　　　　　　　　(h)

FIG. 12. Experimental drawings by adult female chimpanzee
Alpha. (a) Markings spread out
over blank page. (b) Markings
confined to area of central figure.
(c) Markings confined inside
circle of spots. (d) Markings
balance offset square. (e) Markings balance asymmetrical shape.
(f) Markings fill in missing segment of incomplete circle.
(g) Markings fill in missing part
of incomplete pattern. (h) Response to ambiguous figure. (i)
Markings symmetrically placed
around triangle. (After Schiller,
1951)

(i)

Marking of Figures

If a square, a circle, a cross, or some other simple, solid shape was placed on the paper, Alpha marked almost exclusively inside it (Fig. 12b), with only a few hesitant ticks or spots outside it. This result was obtained in twenty-two out of a total of twenty-five such tests.

If the shape was rather small – less than one inch in diameter – a different response was given, the figure being scribbled *over* instead of marked inside. However, the shape, small as it was, was still having some influence. It was the focus of attention of the scribbling and it also eliminated, in twenty out of twenty-one tests, the typical corner-marking tendency seen on blank sheets of paper.

Outline figures, like the larger solid figures, gave rise exclusively to interior marking. As before, there were only a few small ticks and spots outside the edges of the figures. This was so in twenty-two out of twenty-four cases.

When five or more large spots, or small squares, were placed in a tight ring, they acted, in eight out of eight cases, as complete circular figures, all Alpha's scribbling being confined inside the ring (Fig. 12c). If only three or four spots were present, as triangles or squares, then the response was more varied, the large spaces between the spots allowing the pencil lines to escape, so to speak, into the outside spaces.

Balancing the Figures

When a small solid figure was present on the paper in an off-centre position, then Alpha did not mark it, but scribbled instead in the larger open space. This had the effect of balancing the picture (Fig. 12d).

It might be argued that the off-set shape was, in a sense, 'using up' its part of the paper and that Alpha was simply reacting to the remaining space as if it was a smaller blank sheet of paper. But, as Schiller puts it:

There is some reason to believe that this is a genuine tendency to balance masses in the total configuration, since the very strong tendency to draw at the corners and margins of a blank sheet is completely inhibited by the small figure, and the position of her drawing therefore cannot be interpreted merely as a tendency to fill the blank spaces.

In other, more advanced tests, Alpha was offered more complex figures which were themselves asymmetrical (Fig. 12e), and here again she scribbled in such a way that the result was a balancing of the design, although with these more difficult tests she was only successful in 50 per cent of the trials.

Completion of Unfinished Figures

Related, to some extent, to the last tests were several series designed to ascertain whether Alpha would complete an imperfect pattern or shape. She was, for instance, offered a solid circle with a slice missing (Fig. 12f) and, in two of six such tests, she filled in the missing area. In the other four cases she marked the unfinished circle itself.

She succeeded better than this with incomplete patterns. Here, a ring of seven spots, or a square of nine spots, with one spot missing in each case, was presented to her and in every one of eight trials she scribbled in the missing place, thus finishing off the pattern (Fig. 12g).

Crossing of Bold Lines

A completely different response was obtained from Alpha if, instead of a squat figure, a long band or bold line crossed the page. Schiller reported that:

Heavy, single bars across the page induce sweeping marks more or less at right angles to them. In four tests, each with a single black bar, horizontal, vertical, and at forty-five degrees from right and from left, all are crossed by scores of scribbled lines. In three of the four there is not a single line crossing the bar at less than forty-five degrees.

Immediately, the Russian chimpanzee Joni springs to mind (Fig. 2c), for there in Plate XXIII/3 of the Kohts monograph is a drawing which undeniably demonstrates this criss-crossing tendency. Kohts herself modestly described it (p. 557) as 'tracing several intersecting lines', but from a careful examination of the picture it emerges that not only are there far more than 'several' intersections, but that almost all of them consist of short weak lines crossing longer bolder ones. It seems as if the young male Joni was in this case performing naturally what, in Alpha's case, had to be encouraged experimentally.

Other Tendencies

In addition to the tendencies to mark, balance, complete and cross simple figures, Alpha also revealed an interesting negative tendency. If a random arrangement of squares or spots was present on the paper, she did not react to them in any special way. If they were large, she marked each one as a figure by itself. If they were small, she marked around them in the spaces they left. If they were bunched together, she scribbled all over them, treating them as if they were a single figure. The fact that Alpha gave more clear-cut responses to regular figures than to these irregular ones is, of course, very much in line with the findings of Professor Rensch referred to earlier, in which various birds and primates all preferred to select cards with regular patterns drawn on them.

Attempts were also made to find out how she would react to so-called 'ambiguous' figures, of the type sometimes used by human psychologists. The kind used is shown in Fig. 12h. It consisted of a black and white hourglass figure on a green background. In a series of tests with this figure, the black and white areas were inter-changed, sometimes the centre being black and sometimes the top and bottom. It was found that, although Alpha marked all over the figure, she scribbled most in the white areas, in whichever position these happened to be.

Although no indication is given by Schiller of the shade of the green background, it would be a fair guess to say that it was probably dark enough to make the white areas the regions of most intense contrast, to which the ape's pencil would be more strongly attracted.

Finally, there was one series in which Alpha's reactions were almost uncanny. This consisted of hollow triangles, sometimes with circles or other markings included inside them. In five of the seven tests in this triangular series, she not only marked inside the figure, as expected, but also showed a distinct tendency to make symmetrical markings on the *out*side of the triangle, close to and opposite each of its sides (Fig. 12i). This remarkable feat clearly indicates a sense of symmetry and demonstrates it in a completely different way from the picture-balancing results discussed earlier. In both cases the ape was selecting areas for scribbling that resulted in a crude form of aesthetic organization and, to use Schiller's own words:

> Such symmetries might be explained by a tendency to fill in blank spaces and scribble across bars, but the spacing of the marks is significantly different from that filling in around unorganized figures . . . and from the scribbling across bars. The proportion of symmetrically spaced scribbles in the total collection is so great as to argue strongly that Alpha has some feeling for a balance of masses on the page.

Summing up the information obtained from Alpha, it is therefore possible to say that this adult female chimpanzee showed the following composition tendencies:

1. To restrict her scribbling to the surface of the paper.
2. To mark the corners of a blank sheet before filling it in.
3. To mark a central figure.
4. To balance an offset figure.
5. To complete an imperfect figure.
6. To cross strong lines at right angles.
7. To make symmetrical markings around a triangle.

CONGO COMPOSITION TESTS

Because the Schiller tests had only been carried out with a single chimpanzee, it was obviously of great interest to find out whether a second member of this species would give similar results.

As I have already explained, Congo's television duties diverted him considerably from the straight and narrow path of pure research and the test series of experimental drawings were far fewer than they should have been. Furthermore, by the time that work along these more serious lines was gaining momentum, Congo was already not far away from the point when his interest in graphic activities was to be blotted out by a growing passion for brute force. Despite these difficulties it was possible to obtain a total of 172 experimental (8 in. × 13 in.) black and white drawings. Of these, forty were control tests on blank sheets and the remaining 132 were tests where the papers were marked with one or more simple figures. As will be clear from the accompanying illustrations, the test papers, although much the same size as Alpha's, were presented to Congo in the wide, rather than the tall position. This was done because it favoured investigation of the sense of left-right balance in Congo, this particular aspect of ape aesthetics being the one which fascinated me most at the outset.

Distribution of Lines on Blank Papers

When taken as a group, the forty control tests on blank paper reveal several basic tendencies in Congo. In no case, for example, did his drawing wander off the paper to any appreciable extent. He worked very much within the space available and in thirty out of the forty tests he more or less used up the whole of it. In twenty-five instances he virtually covered the whole area, spreading out the position of his lines until the whole space was marked (Fig. 13a and b). In about half the forty tests he showed a tendency to concentrate more lines in the central region of the paper than elsewhere and in eight cases his lines appeared *only* in the central area (Fig. 13c).

In addition to these general tendencies there was also present Congo's speciality, the radiating fan design (see Fig. 14). On fifteen of the blank sheets, the fan patterning element was present to a greater or lesser extent. In some cases, all the lines on the paper were organized into this radiating composition, but in others the fan was only part of the general picture.

The lines of the fan were always spread out across the paper, each one being started separately at the top of the page and drawn towards the chimpanzee. The result was a highly characteristic, roughly symmetrical, rhythmic design. In the earlier drawings it often appeared by itself, but in later sessions it was more frequently combined with curved horizontal scribbles or other markings.

66

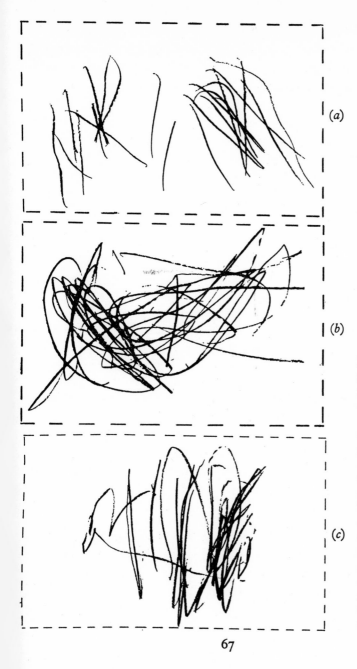

(a)

(b)

(c)

FIG. 13. This and Figs. 14–26 show a selection of the 172 experimental drawings made by Congo. Here the spread-out response to a blank sheet is seen. (*a*) An early example. (*b*) A late example. (*c*) An example showing slight central concentration.

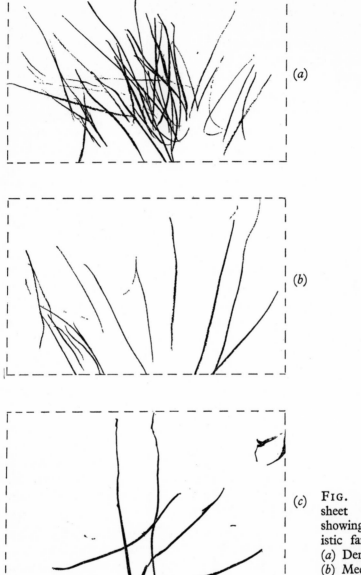

(a)

(b)

(c)

FIG. 14. Blank
sheet responses
showing character-
istic fan patterns.
(a) Dense Fan.
(b) Medium Fan.
(c) Sparse Fan.

As the main interest in the fan pattern is its development and modification and, as this occurred more obviously in the non-experimental paintings and chalk drawings, further discussion of this Congo trademark will be delayed until later. However, it is worth noting here that this tendency was not present in Alpha and she did not in fact show any real organization of her scribbles into a basic design on blank sheets. As mentioned earlier, one fan-pattern drawing was obtained from the chimpanzee Bella, a few imperfect ones from the 'Six-chimp test', and one good one from the capuchin monkey, Pablo, but apart from these cases there are no other records of its occurrence elsewhere.

Returning now to the more general aspects of the blank sheet response, it can be said that Congo showed a strong tendency to fill the space, but without going beyond its boundaries. Simple as this achievement may sound from a human standpoint, it is nevertheless the whole basis of visual composition and its existence in the chimpanzee forms the foundation on which all other compositional tendencies are built. In some of the space-filling cases, the result was achieved with comparatively few lines and it is quite clear that the visual rule governing the drawings in those cases was that of 'mark where you have not already marked'. This rule is not the only one in operation on the blank sheets, however.

In the majority of cases, the page was filled but, as already mentioned, in a few instances there was a concentration on one small area in which all the lines were confined. Here the rule seems to have been the exact opposite, namely 'mark only where you have already marked'. This tendency is clearly seen in the tests where a figure is present on the paper, but in the few cases where it occurred spontaneously it must have been the result of the fact that the first mark made by the chimpanzee acted itself as an object or figure and had sufficient power, so to speak, to attract all the other lines to that spot. Of course, once three or four marks had been made in approximately the same position, their combined appearance would give the effect of a figure being present and then mark after mark would be piled on top, each one strengthening the response more and more.

The reason why this tendency to 'mark where marked' is rare seems to be connected with the size of the initial marking. There is, as we have seen,

69

a strong urge to spread out over the page and to 'mark where *not* marked'. The presence of a bold figure on the paper stimulates an opposing tendency, but only succeeds if the object is large enough to form a powerful focus of interest and to 'trap' the lines. If the object is too small, then the competing tendency to space-fill will dominate the scene and this is what usually happens when the chimpanzee starts from scratch on an empty page. In the exceptional cases, the initial mark may have been a particularly strong one, or the second and third marks may have been inaccurately placed rather near to it to give the effect of a large shape.

It has already been noted that there was an additional tendency to make slightly more marks in the centre of the paper than elsewhere. This applied to many of the thirty cases where there was scribbling over the whole area of the page. Also, in the ten cases where there was a single concentrated area of markings, eight of these were centrally located. Like the preponderance of the radiating fan pattern, this urge to favour the central area of the paper reveals a basic feeling for symmetry in Congo.

Summing up the chimpanzee's reactions to a blank sheet of paper, it is possible to give the following list of the five basic, independent rules by which the animal appears to be abiding:

1. Keep within the space. (40 out of 40 tests.)
2. Mark where you have *not* already marked. (30 out of 40.)
3. Mark where you *have* already marked. (10 out of 40.)
4. Concentrate more on the centre. (24 out of 40.)
5. Mark in a series of radiating lines. (15 out of 40.)

Rules one, four, and five do not conflict with one another, or with rules two and three, but the latter do, of course, compete with each other. It might be argued that, by admitting to the operation of both rule two *and* rule three, one is virtually permitting random marking, since any line, no matter how spatially unorganized, must either be placed according to one rule or the other. But this objection is invalid owing to the extreme forms in which the two tendencies frequently appear. Luckily, circumstances often permit one rule to come into operation in an almost pure form, at the expense of the other, so that it can dominate the scene and clearly expose itself as a basic visual tendency.

Reaction to Rectangles

One of the earliest test series given to Congo was designed to find out more about the self-imposed discipline which prevented him in almost all cases from spreading his scribbles over the edge of the sheet. He was given a set of papers on which rectangles of varying sizes, one per sheet, had been boldly outlined. The largest rectangle was offered first. It was 6 in. × 11 in. and was therefore surrounded by a 1-in. margin. Congo drew inside it and not a single mark appeared outside its edges (Fig. 15a). The second rectangle was 4 in. × 9 in., leaving a 2-in. margin. Congo squeezed his drawing even tighter here, but, although he checked several lines deliberately, just at the edge of the rectangle, one or two did spread over into the larger margin (Fig. 15b). The third rectangle was only 2 in. × 7 in., leaving a huge margin 3-in. wide around it. With this test a fascinating change took place (Fig. 15c). Instead of marking *inside* the shape, Congo repeatedly and rhythmically marked *over* it. Something about it had changed radically for the chimpanzee.

The difference in the response cannot be related entirely to inaccuracy in placing the lines. This may have accounted for the one or two mistakes made with the medium-sized rectangle, but the response to the small rectangle was far too deliberate to be explained in this way. Furthermore, other tests of a completely different nature in which, for example, Congo was successful at putting a key in a lock and opening it, pushing wooden rods into small holes, or inserting coins into slot machines, have confirmed the existence of a surprising accuracy in matters of manual dexterity.

It is quite clear therefore that, for Congo, the small rectangle possessed different properties from the larger ones, apart from its difference in size. The controlling factor appears to be one of ratio of sheet size to rectangle size, for it is only in the case of the small rectangle that the shape is narrower than the margin surrounding it. This difference apparently changes the rectangle, from a *space* to be filled up, into an *object* to be marked over.

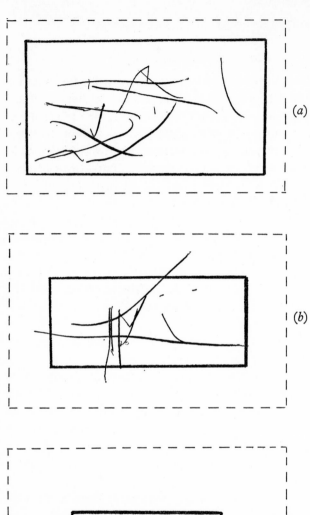

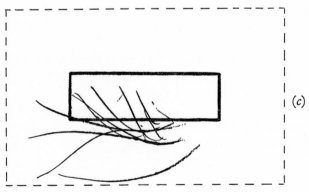

(a)

(b)

(c)

FIG. 15. Reactions to rectangles. A large rectangle (a) is treated like a space and markings confined inside it. This is less successful with a medium rectangle (b), and a small rectangle (c) is marked *over* rather than inside.

72

Marking of a Central Figure

It will be recalled that, in the very first attempt to obtain a drawing from Congo in November 1956, the chimpanzee was given an old piece of cardboard. There was a blot on the board and it was noticed that many of Congo's lines were focused on it (Fig. 2). This was the first clue that Congo, like Alpha, was going to show a tendency to alter the form of his scribbling if an object was present on the paper. During the two years between November 1956 and November 1958, Congo was repeatedly given tests in which a central object was present on the paper and the results obtained confirmed the early suspicions.

Out of thirty-seven tests, involving a variety of single central shapes, Congo modified his scribbles, by condensing almost all of them to the area in and around the objects, in thirty-four, or ninety-two per cent, of the cases.

There were in fact marks on or over the figures in thirty-six of the thirty-seven trials, but in two cases the marks were not deliberately concentrated on the shape in question. In only one of the thirty-seven trials was the central shape completely ignored.

The shapes used were as follows. In twenty-three of the thirty-seven tests, a 2 in. square was presented, either in the form of grey paper glued to the sheet (Fig. 16a and c) or as a boldly drawn black outline (Fig. 16b). There was no apparent difference in response to the solid versus the hollow shape and in all twenty-three cases the squares had lines on, or over, or connected to them, with at most only a few marks in other regions. In eleven of the twenty-three cases, *all* the marks were on or over the figures and the space around was completely avoided.

In five tests a 3-in. hollow circle was given and in all cases the lines were concentrated on the figure (Fig. 17a). In only one of the five were there a few marks away from the circle.

With more complex central figures, such as a hollow cross, or an irregular amoeboid shape, the urge to mark over was reduced but still present. With a differently shaped but simple figure, such as a 2-in. vertical bar $\frac{1}{2}$ in. thick, the tendency was, however, just as strong as with the squares and circles (Fig. 17b).

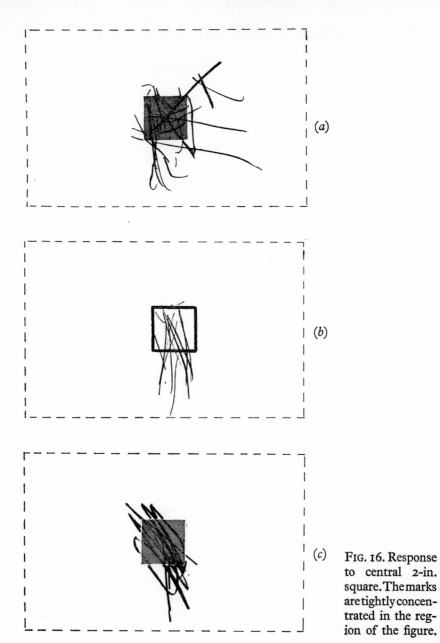

(a)

(b)

(c) FIG. 16. Response to central 2-in. square. The marks are tightly concentrated in the region of the figure.

74

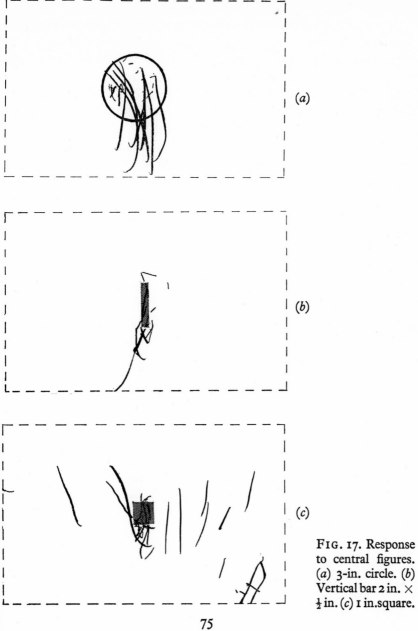

(a)

(b)

(c)

FIG. 17. Response to central figures. (a) 3-in. circle. (b) Vertical bar 2 in. × ½ in. (c) 1 in. square.

An interesting difference in response occurred if the size of the central square was reduced to 1 in. (Fig. 17c) or ½ in. This change appeared to reduce its significance to a point where it was even completely ignored. It was stated earlier that, in thirty-four of the thirty-seven central-figure-tests, there was a concentration of lines in the region of the figure. It is with these small-sized figures that the three odd results were obtained, one with the 1-in. square and two with the ½-in. square.

From all this it gradually emerged that there was an optimum size for a figure for the chimpanzee, as far as 'object valence' was concerned. A figure apparently had three properties according to its size in relation to the size of the sheet of paper:

A large figure was a space (to be marked inside).

A medium figure was an object (to be marked over).

A small figure was a spot (to be ignored).

In the last of these three there was less consistency than with the other two, the small space sometimes acting as a focus of scribbling, but this is in line with the results obtained with blank sheets where, on rare occasions, a small initial mark 'caught the eye' of the chimpanzee, as it were, and trapped the lines.

Response to Multiple Figures

The tests with blank sheets showed that there was a tendency to favour the central area of the paper and it might be argued that this would account for the marking of a central object. A detailed comparison of the two sets of results nevertheless revealed that the degree of concentration was far greater in figure cases than in blank ones and that although the centrality of the figures naturally must have favoured their being marked, it only accounted for a small proportion of the lines drawn on or over them. But to investigate this point further, Congo was given a series of eight tests with two or three figures present.

In six of the eight tests he marked each of the squares in turn and quite deliberately. The presence of more than one shape on the paper appeared to fascinate him and, instead of the usual bold scribbling, the squares received gentle check-marks. It was almost as if Congo was autographing them.

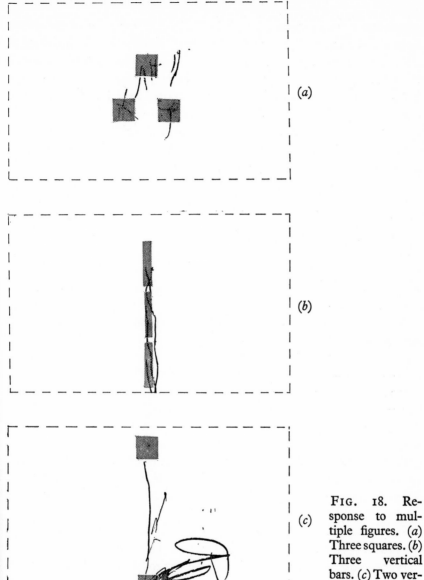

(a)

(b)

(c)

FIG. 18. Response to multiple figures. (a) Three squares. (b) Three vertical bars. (c) Two vertically arranged squares.

This performance was given to two rectangles, two squares, and a triangle of three squares (Fig. 18a) arranged, in each case, symmetrically about the centre of the page. When three thin bars were placed, one above the other, down the middle of the page, Congo proceeded with great care to join them up with several vertical lines down their length (Fig. 18b). This surprising response was repeated when two squares were placed, one at the top and the other at the bottom of the centre of the page (Fig. 18c). The chimpanzee's immediate reaction was to make a bold vertical line down the middle of the page. These two 'joining' responses were practically unique in the whole of Congo's work.

Having established a strong object-marking urge in Congo, as distinct from a simple centre-preference, it remained to be seen how these two tendencies would fare if put into competition with one another. A series of three tests was used for this purpose, in which two 2-in. squares were separated more and more from the middle of the page, one going to the left and the other to the right. The results can be seen clearly in Figs. 19a, b and c.

Both squares were marked with check-lines in each case, but when they were separated half-way, the lines began to stray slightly into the larger and more inviting central space. When the squares were pulled right apart, they were still each given some attention, but the central area was now too attractive to be left alone and a bold central concentration of scribble was added.

It was clear from this test that Congo's interests were being divided between the urge to mark the objects and the urge to fill the space. These two aims are not, of course, incompatible, as was revealed by the last test, and the animal can easily answer both calls, but it robs him of his single-mindedness. It puts him in a position where one interest is likely to obliterate the other, not by incompatibility, but simply by competing for his primary attention.

Where there is a bold figure and an inferior space, or vice versa, there will be no problem, but where both are attractive, he may follow the urge to mark, or to fill up, or he may do both. To test this further, he was given a large series of tests in which one square only was placed on the paper and which was always offset either to the left or to the right.

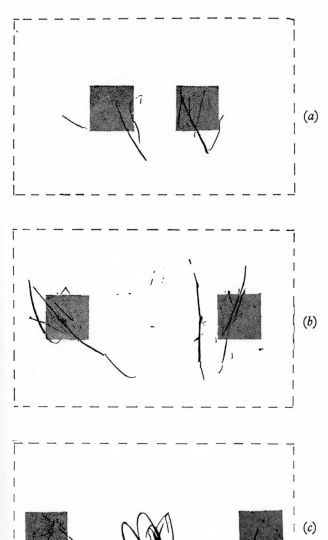

(a)

(b)

(c)

FIG. 19. Double-square test, show-ing the change in response as the two figures are separated. In (c) the central space is too large to be ignored.

Left-right Balance

Given a test with a single offset figure, there were four possible responses Congo could make:

1. To mark the offset square only.
2. To balance the square by filling the offset space only.
3. To mark *and* to balance.
4. To scribble without apparent reference to the special situation.

Altogether thirty-three left-right balance tests were made using 2-in. squares and the results were as follows:

1. Mark only: 3 (see Fig. 21a).
2. Balance only: 11 (see Fig. 20).
3. Mark and Balance: 16 (see Fig. 21 b and c).
4. Unclassifiable: 3.

In thirty of the thirty-three cases there was therefore a distinct response to the test and in only three of these thirty did the chimpanzee ignore the unbalanced nature of the situation. In the other twenty-seven responses (82 per cent) there was a definite tendency to balance the square, the latter sometimes being marked and sometimes left alone.

The frequency of object-marking was only nineteen out of thirty-three cases, or 58 per cent, as compared with 92 per cent when the figures were centrally placed. An offset square is therefore only two-thirds as attractive as a central one, or, to put it another way, it could be said that one-third of the 'marking-appeal' of a central figure is its centrality.

One other fact to emerge from these results is that the two tendencies, to fill the space and to mark the figure, competed (fourteen times) almost as often as they combined (sixteen times), but, when competing, the urge to fill the space dominated the urge to mark in most (eleven out of fourteen) cases.

A similar, but shorter, series of (twelve) tests was carried out using 1-in. squares. The smaller figure was less powerful as an attraction for marking, but still created sufficient impact to stimulate balancing. Nine out of the twelve tests showed balancing marks, six opposite unmarked and three opposite marked squares. In no case was the square alone marked. There

PLATE 19. Congo painting showing stiff-bristle technique.
(*Collection Roland Penrose, London.*)

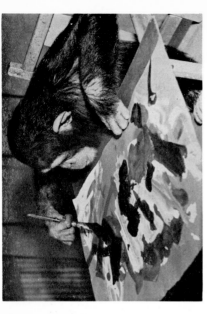

PLATE 20. Congo using left hand (advanced grip).

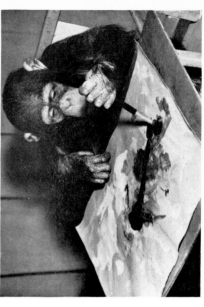

PLATE 21. Congo using right hand (advanced grip.)

PLATE 22. Primitive grip, with thumb pointing

PLATE 23. Primitive grip, with thumb up.

PLATE 24. Intermediate grip.

PLATE 25. Irrelevant actions appear at low intensities.

PLATE 26. Congo making a standardized experimental drawing.

PLATE 27. The dust from pastels produces strange facial expressions.

PLATE 28. Simple central fan pattern. (*Collection Princess Zeid, London.*)

PLATE 29. Twisted fan pattern. (*Collection William Copley, Long-point-sur-Orage.*)

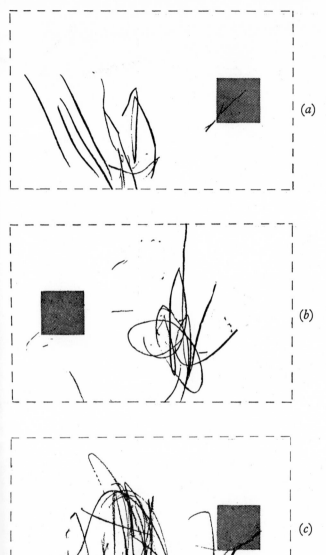

(a)

(b)

(c)

FIG. 20. Left-right balance tests. When the figure is offset, the markings appear opposite it, producing a crude balance.

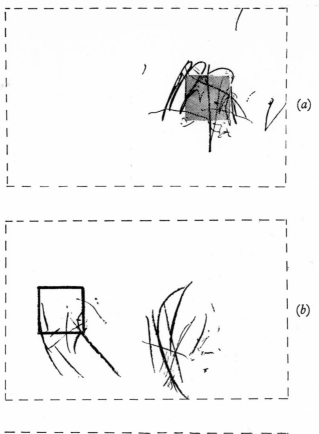

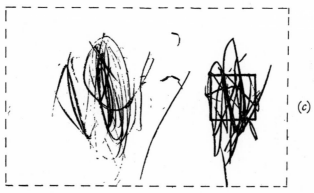

(a)

(b)

(c)

FIG. 21. Simple balance responses are not always given. Sometimes (a) the tendency to mark the shape dominates the tendency to balance. Sometimes (b and c) both tendencies are expressed in the same drawing.

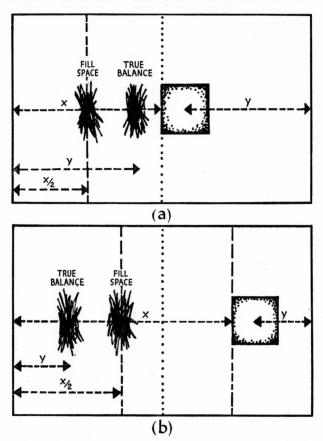

(a)

(b)

FIG. 22. Diagram showing two types of balancing used by Congo. When the figure was slightly offset (*a*) Congo's markings were equally offset in the opposite direction, giving a true balance response. But when the figure was strongly offset (*b*) Congo's markings appeared in the centre of the large empty space left by the square's displacement. (*Note:* In 'slightly offset' cases the 'filling-space' point is outside the balance point. In 'greatly offset' cases, it is inside it.)

were three results which could not be classified in this series, the higher proportion of these also probably being due to the less imposing figure.

Space-filling versus True Balance

Up to this point, the words 'balancing' and 'filling' have been used interchangeably. At a crude level of analysis this is permissible because filling up an empty space on one side of a picture is bound to *assist* in balancing it. A more accurate balance can, of course, be achieved by a different process, which I shall call 'true balance', and which must now be analysed as a separate entity.

If Congo was using the crude method of filling up a space, then one would expect his scribble to be centred on the middle of the large space left vacant by the offset square. This is predicted because it is known that in his responses to blank sheets, Congo has shown a distinct tendency to favour the centre of the page. If, on the other hand, the animal possesses a true sense of balance, then the compensating scribble opposite the offset figure, should be *equally offset*.

In those tests where Congo scribbled in one concentrated patch with a recognizable focal point, it is possible to measure the position of this point on the page and ascertain which of the two rules he was obeying.

This was possible in sixteen of the tests and the results were most unexpected. It was anticipated that he was either working always to one rule, or always to the other, but this was not so.

Before continuing it must be explained that the squares in these tests were not all offset to the same degree. Some were only displaced 1 in. or 2 in. to one side or other of the page centre, whilst others were 3 in., or even 4 in. away from the mid-line. If the 1-in. and 2-in. displacements are referred to as 'slightly offset' and the 3-in. and 4-in. cases as 'strongly offset' and the results are given separately for these two groups, then they reveal that Congo was employing two different methods of balancing on the two occasions.

Of the sixteen analysable tests, six were with 'slightly' offset figures and ten were with 'strongly' offset ones. Of the six slight offset cases, four were genuinely balanced to within $\frac{1}{2}$ in. and the other two were less than 1 in. away from the balance point. Of the ten strongly offset cases, six of the scribble patches were accurately placed to within $\frac{1}{2}$ in. of the space centre

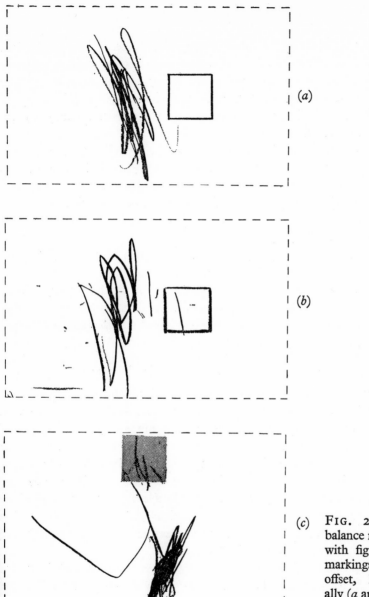

(a)

(b)

(c)   FIG. 23. True
balance responses
with figures and
markings equally
offset, horizont-
ally (*a* and *b*) and
vertically (*c*).

and three more were less than 1 in. away. One was badly placed so that it neither filled the centre of the open space, nor balanced the figure position.

These striking results came, as I have said, as a complete surprise. They show that, when the open space is big enough, with the square pushed right over to one side, then the chimpanzee reacts to it *as* a space and treats it accordingly by concentrating in its central area (see Figs. 20 and 21b and c.).

If, on the other hand, the square is only slightly off-centre, there is no single big space to dominate the scene and here the animal reveals his genuine sense of balance by offsetting his scribbles to the same degree as the figure, but in the opposite direction (see Figs. 23a and 23b).

Vertical Balance

Two tests were given in which a 2-in. square was placed centrally, but either at the top or the bottom of the page. In one case Congo marked the square in the usual way, but in the other test he amazed me by a quite deliberate vertical balancing of the figure. This test can be seen in Fig. 23c and is one of the most remarkable compositional results obtained from Congo.

Loss of Graphic Balancing during Filming

In the spring of 1958 a film was made demonstrating Congo's painting and drawing achievements and one of the aspects I wished to record was, naturally, the remarkable balance-response. But a strange development occurred which interfered with this. All the tests made with Congo that are referred to elsewhere in this chapter were carried out under strictly controlled and standardized conditions, as described in Chapter 2. Distractions were kept to a minimum. When Congo was expected to perform in a film studio, surrounded by film technicians and with all the fascinating paraphernalia of cinematography, he was more absorbed by the intriguing environment than by the work in hand.

It is true that previously he had painted on television several times, but painting had always fascinated him more than drawing, and he painted happily for the filming also.

But, when it came to experimental drawings, his attention soon started to wander. He responded to a blank sheet excellently and he marked centrally placed squares in his usual way, but when it came to the balance tests with offset squares, his concentration was not high enough. Instead of the typical compensating scribble opposite the figure, he simply marked it and then abandoned work.

Fifteen experimental drawings were made for the film and seven of them involved an off-centre figure. In only two did he balance it. In the other five he did no more than mark over it. In the standard tests, under controlled conditions, he had only failed to balance on three occasions and had succeeded in twenty-seven. The startling shift in the balance ratio from 27/3, to 2/5 under inferior experimental conditions, indicates that the graphic balance response must require a high degree of concentration.

In standard tests, both before and after the filming period, the balance response was strongly present and its domination of the simpler marking-over tendency on those occasions reveals that they must have involved a high intensity response on the part of the chimpanzee.

Intersecting Bars

Alpha had shown a strong inclination to cross boldly-drawn lines, or bars, at right angles and this tendency was also shown by the Russian chimpanzee Joni (Fig. 1c). Congo was given eighteen tests for this response, but showed it fully in only one of them (Fig. 24a). He did not give it as a response to multiple bars, either vertically, diagonally, or horizontally arranged. He did show it, several times, in a low intensity form, when offered a test paper on which one bold single vertical line was placed. On one of these papers he performed it at high intensity with unmistakable deliberation.

While giving him these single vertical bar tests, left-right shifts of the line were made in a few cases and the results were striking (Figs. 24b and 24c). As soon as the line was appreciably moved to the left, then all but a few check marks were confined to the right, and vice versa. It was as if the chimpanzee was treating the line, not as a very thin object to be marked,

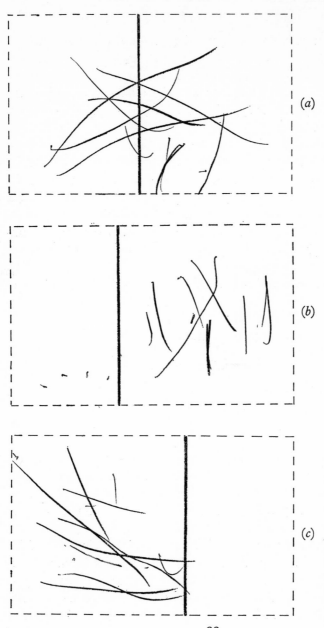

(a)

(b)

(c)

Fig. 24. Intersection response. This was rarely given by Congo. It is seen in (a) but in (b) and (c), with the vertical bar off-centre, it is displaced by a different response (*see text*, p. 87).

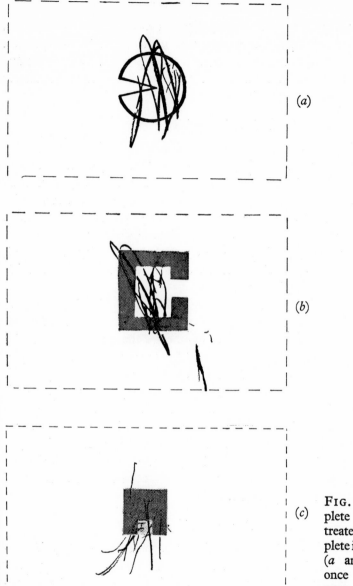

(a)

(b)

(c)

FIG. 25. Incomplete figures are treated as if complete in most cases (a and b), but once (c) Congo gave the completion response.

but as a cut down the paper, dividing it into a smaller and a larger portion. What is so interesting is that Congo then made an all-or-none choice. Instead of distributing lines proportionally according to the size of the two spaces, he made an all-out choice for the larger one and at the almost complete expense of the smaller one.

Completion of Unfinished Figures

Another of Alpha's tests had been to complete an imperfect or unfinished figure and Congo was also given nine trials of this type. He invariably marked over the whole object and did not therefore make any distinction between complete and incomplete shapes. The shapes used were a 2 in. square with a section cut out, a 3 in. circle with a segment missing, and a hollow rectangle with part of one side missing. In eight of the nine tests, the shapes were treated as if they were completed forms (Figs. 25a and b), but with one of the figures Congo did concentrate his markings in the region of the missing section (Fig. 25c).

The reason for this is simple enough. To Congo the figure was an object on the page and the missing section was, so to speak, an *object on the figure*. In other words, one was in reality offering the chimpanzee a choice of two focal points, a large-scale one and a small-scale one. In simpler tests, where Congo was offered a single complete square on the paper, it was found that, for him, there was an optimum square-size of approximately 2 in. and that, if the square was smaller, it was less attractive as an object to be marked. In the cases of the incomplete figures, he was virtually being offered a focal choice between an optimally-sized object (the incomplete figure) and a sub-optimal object (the missing section). The eight-to-one results in favour of the larger figure are not therefore out of line with the other Congo results.

Corner Marking

The detailed scoring of the corners of a blank sheet held a strong fascination for Alpha. It also occurred in Congo's drawings, but less frequently and on different occasions. Alpha marked all four corners and always confined this activity to empty pages. If experimental figures were present on the paper, the corners were completely ignored. Also, the corner-marking always preceded the central scribbling.

Congo's corner-marking differed in all these details. Firstly, it was never seen to occur on any of the forty blank sheets used in the tests. Out of the total number of 172 tests, distinct corner-marking was only observed in six instances and in each of these there was a figure present on the paper. Secondly, Congo never marked more than one of the four corners. In all six cases, it was a lower corner that received the benefit of his attention (three on the left and three on the right). Finally, the corner-scribbling usually followed the marking of the experimental figure. In four of the six cases, the figure present was offset, in the other two it was central. Two of the offset tests had the figure to the right and the corner marked was then the bottom left. The other two offset tests had the figure on the left side of the page and there the corner-markings were in the bottom right corner opposite. In the two central cases, one had the bottom left corner marked and the other the bottom right.

Another interesting feature of Congo's corner-marking urge was that it showed a peak period. From August to October 1957, fifty experimental drawings were obtained. From December 1957 to February 1958, seventy-nine tests were made, and from April to November 1958, there were forty-two. All six of the corner-marking cases appeared in the middle period.

From the three selected examples of this corner-marking tendency in Congo (Fig. 26a, b and c), it can be seen that it interfered to some extent with the business of balancing the picture, although, as was noted above, the corner chosen was always the one opposite the off-centre square.

The explanation of corner-marking is probably that it represents a response to an inferior focal point, made by the sharp meeting at right angles of two of the sides of the paper. If this is true, then it is easy to understand why Congo's corner-marking was so infrequent, although it is not so easy to see why it should have occurred when figures were present rather than on blank pages. When a figure is present, it offers better focal points for scribbling, and, with Alpha, who corner-marked blank sheets, this was enough to obliterate the corner response completely.

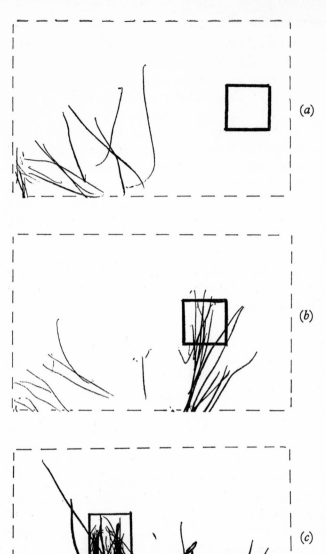

FIG. 26. Corner-marking. Like Alpha, Congo showed this special response, but unlike her he only marked one corner in any one picture. Sometimes it was the bottom left corner (a and b), sometimes the bottom right (c).

(a)

(b)

(c)

92

The only difference between the two apes that might explain this is the presence in Congo alone of the strong fan-pattern urge on empty sheets. This frequent and competing line-arrangement may perhaps help to account for the ignoring of the corners by Congo.

Scattered Spots

When given a page scattered with thirteen small circles, Congo marked seven of them with lines. Almost every one of these lines started on or near the edge of one of these seven circles. It did not appear that he was reacting to the mass of circles as such, but simply to each circle as a separate entity, as did Alpha in similar tests.

Changes in Style during Experimental Period

Alpha was tested for six months, Congo for two years. During Alpha's test period it was noticed that her drawings developed from short, nervous lines to longer, bolder, and often connected lines, or 'line-bundles'. A more detailed account of Congo's changes will be given in the next chapter, as most of them concern his calligraphy rather than his composition. But one comment is relevant here. That is that the change from short, simple lines, over to more complex loops, bundles and spirallings, which took place as time went on, although basically a calligraphic change, nevertheless influenced the quality of Congo's composition. For the more complex the shape of the lines, the less attention was paid to their spatial arrangement.

Luckily this interference did not become serious until towards the end of Congo's picture-making period, after most of the experimental series had been completed. It did, however, reduce considerably the aesthetic value of his last few series of paintings.

After a rest of fifteen months, Alpha was tested again for her drawing responses and it was found that she had reverted during that time to her earlier style. Congo has, as I write, been a year without painting or drawing and it remains to be seen whether, in the months to come, he will be sufficiently manageable to be tested again and to find out whether he too has regressed in style.

93

FIG. 27. The first fan pattern produced by Congo.

Development of the Fan Pattern

I have already referred to the fact that Congo's trademark, the radiating fan pattern, appeared more strikingly in the non-experimental pictures than in the standardized tests and so, in considering its development over the two-year period, it is necessary to examine the total output of the animal, rather than the experimental sections alone. When this is done, it emerges that the fan pattern appeared in over ninety of the 384 pictures made by Congo (roughly 24 per cent). Sometimes it appeared by itself, sometimes as part of a more complex patterning.

The first fan motifs appeared on December 8th, 1956 (Fig. 27) and the last on November 9th, 1958. They occurred throughout the whole picture-making period, in pencil drawings, pastels, crayon drawings, brush paintings and even (Plates E and F) in the few finger-paintings.

In most of the early examples, the fan patterns were simple and unadorned. Usually they were centrally placed on the page (Plate 28) and filled the area of the paper, whether it was small or large. If, by some initial maladjustment, Congo started a simple fan slightly to one side of the page centre, he would then urgently attempt to correct the error by stretching out the lines on one side to fill the page as best he could (Plate G).

The number of lines that made up a fan pattern varied between forty and six and it was noticeable that the fans with the largest number of lines were usually those drawn with thin pencil points, whereas those made using a thick paint-brush usually had far fewer lines. It seems as if the strength of the visual feed-back from the fan-line just completed was important in determining the degree to which the arm was shifted to the side, ready to make the next line in the pattern. A bold fan-line made with a thick brush sent back a powerful visual message which had the effect of displacing the animal's arm farther than if a thin weak line was produced.

The angles of the lines and the relationships of these angles to the positions of the lines were analysed and it was found that, in many cases, if the fan was projected downwards the lines would have met at a point that was approximately the centre of the chimpanzee's body, as it sat at its picture-making. This fact, combined with the observation that each of the fan-pattern lines was started at the top of the page and progressed towards the animal, immediately suggested a possible biological significance for the pattern. If a young chimpanzee is given a loose mass of bedding material such as straw or hay, it will sit in the centre of it and then gather in towards its body handful after handful until it has a circular bed, or nest, packed tight around its body. If the bed is weak in one spot, it will adjust this by stretching out and pulling an extra handful into that area. This bed-making routine has several points of similarity with the drawing of a fan-pattern. In the first place, the arm goes through a similar series of stretches and bends in each instance. In one case it marks a line towards itself, in the other, it pulls a wad of straw towards itself, In both cases the movements are radially arranged and in both cases there is a visual feed-back controlling the degree of displacement from movement to movement. (In the bed-making case there will also be an important tactile feed-back from the bedding packed around the animal's body.) Also, in both activities, the animal can stop, and then continue the action again after a pause, starting again from where it left off. In fan drawings, it was sometimes observed that Congo would stop (perhaps because of a broken pencil point, or because of some distraction) and might then continue and complete the pattern *using the other hand*. A similar shift was also seen in bed-making.

These similarities point very strongly to the conclusion that the origin of the fan pattern is tied up with the apparently inborn action of bed-making. This is not to suggest that drawing a fan shape is in any way a kind of 'substitute' bed-making action, but rather that there is a predisposition for this type of rhythmic response already built into the chimpanzee system that favours the production of this type of pattern.

The arguments against this view cannot be overlooked. In the first place, fan patterns have only been produced by four out of the twenty-three chimpanzees that have drawn or painted. Bed-making is a fundamental response of all chimpanzees, as far as is known, and it would be expected that, if it influenced the picture-making of one, it would influence all in the same way. Secondly, the creation of a perfect fan pattern by a capuchin monkey can be cited as giving a wider significance to the action than can be explained by the inborn specialities of one species. However, it is not impossible that the fan pattern created by the capuchin originated in a totally different way and is a purely convergent phenomenon. Perhaps the capuchin even has a similar form of bed-making routine.

If the arguments against the bed-making theory seem stronger than those in favour of it, there is another possible explanation of the fan pattern phenomenon which may commend itself. This is the theory of 'mechanical simplicity'. Industrial psychologists, studying the way in which factory-workers snip ends, twist pins, sort knobs, or clip strips, often come to the conclusion that the activity under review is being performed in an in-

Split fan patterns by Congo. *Above*, with a central yellow spot (*Collection Sir Herbert Read, Yorkshire*) and *below*, with a central black spot.

efficient and unnecessarily complex manner. If the ends were snipped sideways instead of upwards, they report, or if the pins were twisted outwards instead of inwards, the mechanical simplicity of the arm movements of the workers would be improved by five per cent. Using this approach, it might be argued that Congo and the capuchin and the other fan-pattern makers were only using the simplest mechanical movements of their arms to fill the spaces in front of them.

This does not, of course, mean that the fan shape is nothing more than a motoric exercise with no visual organization. The fact that the fan fits the paper, be it large or small, and that a fan can be stopped and then started again after a pause, reveals that the pattern is under visual discipline. But the selection of this particular pattern, by both capuchin and chimpanzee, does give some weight to the argument that motoric simplicity may be the controlling factor.

It may eventually emerge that the demands of motoric simplicity influenced the bed-making and fan patterns independently, but in a similar way. Alternatively, these demands may have influenced the nature of bed-making movements during evolution and then the form of the now fixed bed-making pattern could, in turn, have influenced the fan construction.

But, whichever view is favoured, the explanation is only a partial one, concerning no more than the origin of the pattern. For, once Congo became familiar with the fan shape, its production became, in its turn, a fixed unit of behaviour, available for modification and embellishment.

Two startling examples of the use of the fan as a *fixed visual unit* were the 'reverse fan' (Fig. 28) and the 'subsidiary fan' (Plate J). The creation of the reverse fan was one of those rare moments of pure creativeness, where the experimenter could hardly believe his eyes. As I have said, Congo produced over ninety fan patterns, always starting each line at its far point and drawing it towards himself. On the day in question, Congo had drawn several normal fan patterns in the usual way (Fig. 29) and then, as the next blank card was placed in front of him, a strange intensity seemed to overtake him and with soft, almost inaudible grunts he began laboriously to make a fan, starting each line at a near and central point and spreading it away from him. As each line was marked out, he could be seen carefully

FIG. 28. Reversed fan pattern. Of the ninety fan patterns produced by Congo, this was the only one in which each line was drawn from the bottom upwards.

studying its course, so that it radiated away in a fresh direction from those already made.

The fan was therefore similar in appearance to any normally produced one, but had been drawn completely in reverse. This astonishing performance can only be explained if one assumes that Congo had reached the stage where he had a *fan image* in his brain and that he was virtually experimenting with a new way of producing it.

The subsidiary fan example gives further proof of this. In this picture (Plate J), Congo had already painted a rather ineffectual main fan and then, towards the end of the picture, took a brush of black paint and quite deliberately, with five rhythmically delivered strokes, formed a perfect, small, off-centre, subsidiary fan-shape. The focal point is not only to

98

FIG. 29. Fan pattern produced at the same session as the reversed fan (Fig. 28), but in this case produced in the usual way, with the lines drawn from the top downwards.

one side of the centre of the picture, but it is also *within* the area of the picture and does not therefore correspond with the position of the animal's body.

Further proof of the emancipation of the fan pattern as a visual unit in its own right, independent from its origins, was forthcoming in Congo's later paintings. Every so often he would try out new distortions or extensions and some of these resulted in his most exciting pictures.

During September 1957 he produced a series of 'stippled fan-bundles' (Plates 30, 31 and 32). These consisted of a basic fan, sometimes rather reduced, with a strong, solid base, the latter being overmarked with bold spotting. Then, in the winter of 1957–8, he introduced the 'split fan',

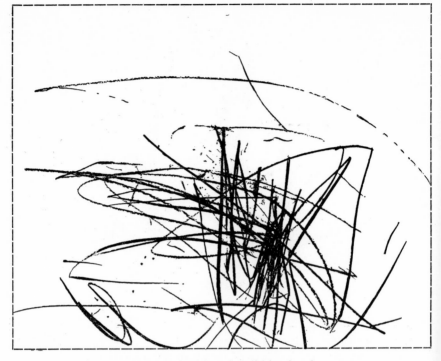

FIG. 30. Multiple-horizontal scribble plus fan pattern.

where the centre lines were ruthlessly omitted and replaced by a single bold spot or blob (Plates H and I). Eventually, as he grew larger, the base of the fan became curved more and more, the centre lines returning but stopping shorter than the side lines (Plate 34).

Later still, as the horizontal motifs began to run riot and obliterate the fan shapes there was, in the summer of 1958, a series of 'horizontal-multiples plus fan' (Plate 35 and Fig. 30). Even after the horizontals had led him into the world of loops and spirals, an occasional fan would crop up in a session and then, for the first time, there appeared the 'double-lined or looped fan', with the lines drawn out and then in again in one sophisticated movement, leaving the hand ready for the next action (Fig. 31).

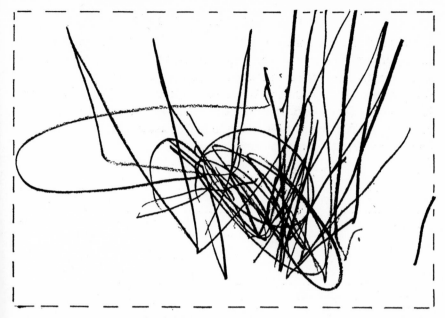

FIG. 31. Loop-fan pattern. Each of the fan lines has become a double stroke, out-and-in.

This elaborate variation on a fan theme by Congo is unparalleled in ape picture-making and leaves one in no doubt as to the sensitivity of the chimpanzee's inventiveness.

Other fan-makers, such as the capuchin Pablo (Plate 8) and the chimpanzees Bella (Fig. 4), Josie (Fig. 5) and Fifi (Fig. 8), produced only simple fans, starting in each case, as far as I know, from the top and drawing the lines towards themselves, as did Congo in his typical pictures. Of course, none of these other animals was tested over a long period of time and it would be fascinating to select one of these or another fan-making individual and follow him or her through several years of picture production to find out whether variations of such a theme occurred again and whether they were similar to those made by Congo.

COMPOSITION COMPARISONS

Although we have a few experimental results from other sources, namely Sophie the gorilla, some human children, and a group of six briefly tested chimpanzees, these series are too short to be included in a detailed table of comparisons. At the present stage, only Alpha and Congo have been investigated fully enough, as far as compositional tendencies are concerned, but, even so, it is worth tabulating the major results obtained from these two chimpanzees, for comparative purposes.

Similarities between Alpha and Congo

TEST	ALPHA	CONGO
1. Restrict drawing to area of paper	Almost always	Almost always
2. Mark corners	All four corners of blank sheets	One lower corner only (6/172)
3. Mark blank paper with fan pattern	No	Yes (15/40)
4. Mark central solid figure	Yes (22/25)	Yes (34/37)
5. Mark within outline figure	Yes (22/24)	Yes (34/37)
6. Mark inside close field of five or more spots	Yes (8/8)	—
7. Mark each of two or three figures	—	Yes (6/8)
8. Balance offset figure	Yes	Yes (27/33)
9. Balance asymmetrical figure	Yes (50%)	—
10. Complete unfinished figure	Sometimes (2/6)	Once (1/9)
11. Complete unfinished pattern	Yes (8/8)	Once (1/9)
12. Cross heavy bars at right angles	Yes (4/4)	Once (1/14)
13. Absence of special reaction to scattered spots	Yes	Yes
14. Mark symmetrically around triangle	Yes (5/7)	—

It is clear from this table that in most of the responses the two animals were very similar, but that also each has its own peculiarities, Alpha's speciality being corner marking and figure completion and Congo's being the fan pattern. (The figures given in the table refer to the number of times a response appeared in relation to the number of trials in a series, wherever these facts are known.)

Experimental Drawings by Sophie

The valuable series of twenty experimental drawings obtained from Sophie, the adult female gorilla at the Rotterdam Zoo, provide some strikingly similar results to those obtained in the full-scale tests reported above.

Sophie was given five blank sheets, four central 2 in. squares, eight offset squares, one double square, one central vertical bar and one incomplete circular figure.

Of the five blank sheets, three show overall scribblings (Fig. 32) that fit the page and two show central concentrations. There were no corner markings and no fan patterns, but all her drawings showed a very characteristic, jerky, zigzag scribbling. This scribbling style was so distinctive that no Congo drawing, for example, could ever be confused with a Sophie, but this will be discussed further in the next chapter.

The four central squares all received special attention from Sophie (Fig. 33) and the concentration of markings on the figures is very similar indeed to that shown by Alpha and Congo. The incomplete circular figure offered to her was also in a central position and this too is marked in the same way, but not completed. Here again Sophie reacted in the same way as Congo.

With the eight offset figures, Sophie showed different reactions from those of the two chimpanzees. She did *not* reveal a high frequency of balance responses. In seven of the eight tests she marked the square (Fig. 34a) and in one (Fig. 34b) only did she ignore it and mark in the space opposite.

In the case of the central vertical line she did not show any tendency to cross it at right angles and seems to have ignored it, marking right across the page.

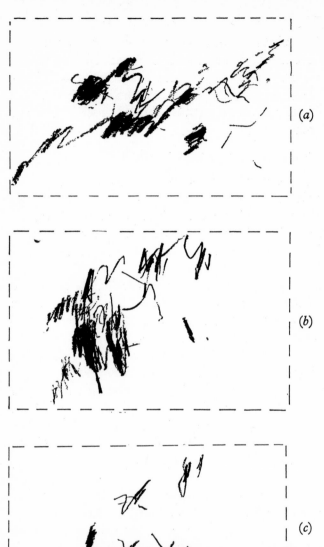

(a)

(b)

(c)

FIG. 32. Experimental drawings by adult gorilla Sophie. On blank sheets there is an overall pattern of small-amplitude zig-zags.

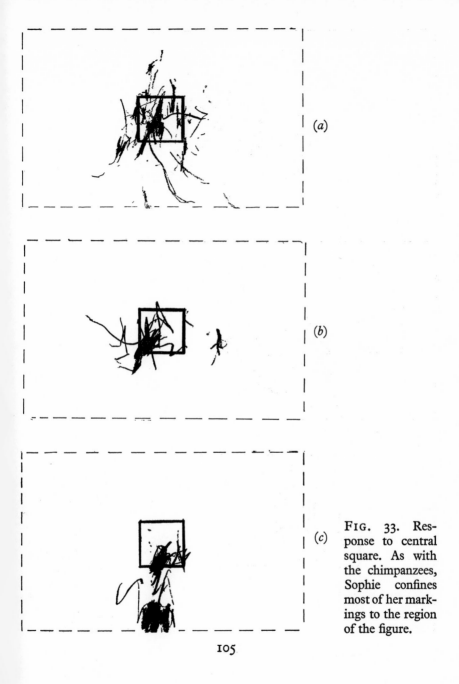

(a)

(b)

(c)

FIG. 33. Response to central square. As with the chimpanzees, Sophie confines most of her markings to the region of the figure.

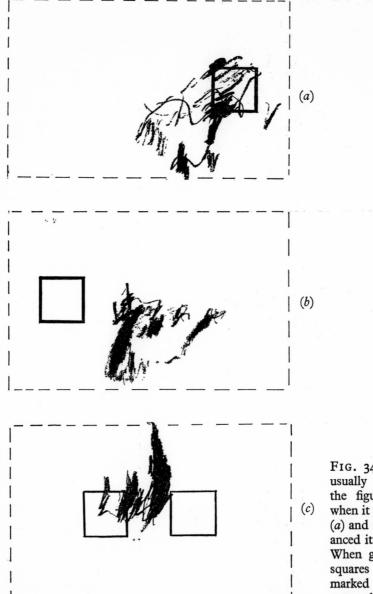

(a)

(b)

(c)

FIG. 34. Sophie usually marked the figure, even when it was offset (a) and only balanced it once (b). When given two squares (c), she marked in between them.

106

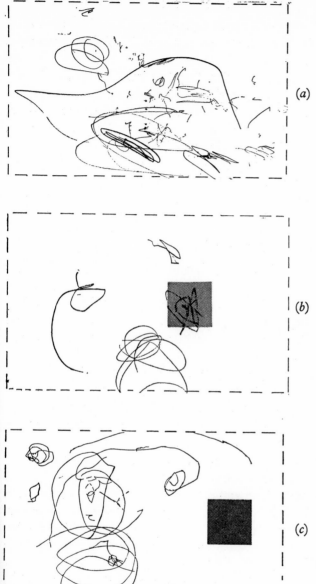

(a)

(b)

(c)

FIG. 35. Human infant tests with (a) blank sheet, (b and c) offset squares.

Where she was presented with two squares, she marked between them (Fig. 34c) instead of inside each one, as was expected on the basis of Congo's response to this test.

Summing up, it can be said that Sophie shows the powerful basic responses of filling up a page and of marking an object, but that she does not show the more subtle reactions of balancing, completing or crossing. It is, of course, a very unfair comparison, as far as test *failures* are concerned, because both Alpha and Congo, although they cannot be said to have undergone any actual training, were subjected to long periods of familiarization with the problem. It is, in fact, surprising that Sophie showed as much detailed response as she did with only twenty experimental papers completed.

Human Infant Tests

As with Sophie the gorilla, a young human was also given a short test series of experimental papers with the same proportions and figures. He was presented with a set of thirteen papers, which he completed on various occasions between the age of one year eight months and one year eleven months (see Fig. 35). Three of the sheets were blanks, two had central squares and eight had offset squares.

Only three of the ten squares were deliberately marked and even in these cases the markings were not confined to the region of the figure. One of the two central squares was ignored completely. In only two of the eight off-centre tests was there any real attempt to balance the picture and even then it was simply as a 'larger-space fill-in' response.

These results are typical of human infants, as is their undoubtedly superior calligraphy. It seems that the young *Homo sapiens* is worse than the chimpanzee at composition and design, but at the same time is much better at calligraphic exploration. The advanced state of the latter may to some extent be the explanation of the inferior composition results. The human child is so fascinated by the many diverse courses that lines can be made to follow (what Paul Klee referred to as 'taking a line for a walk') that he becomes absorbed in this game, often finishing one small scribble on the page and then excitedly moving on to a second variation in any other near-by space that comes easily to hand. Each scribble is created almost without reference to its environment. It is this preference, in human infants, for calligraphy over composition that leads, as we shall see in the next chapter, to the ultimate creation of the first representational images, a phase never yet reached by an ape.

A possible clue to the reason for this difference is suggested by a statement by Kortlandt. In contrasting man and the apes, he remarks that 'In man's world things are characterized predominantly by their nature (or "thatness") because the live prey wanders to and fro; whereas in the ape's world things are characterized predominantly by their place ("thereness") because their food grows at fixed places'. Kortlandt was not discussing picture-making nor could he have been aware of the differences in calligraphic and compositional achievements in man and apes, as they are being set out in this book for the first time.

This independent suggestion of his, concerning the 'thereness', or spatial arrangement, in apes and the 'thatness', or awareness of the details of objects in man, is, however, highly stimulating when applied in a pictorial context.

The 'Six-chimp' Test

In addition to the intensive testing of Congo, I also carried out a brief experiment using six young chimpanzees which, although used to human company, did not know me personally very well and had not previously had any experience of drawing or painting. As already explained the main object of this test was, in the first instance, to find out how many individuals showed an interest in the activity and how many ignored it and would take no notice. When, in the initial tests on blank cards, it was found that five of the six were immediately fascinated and concentrated hard on their picture-making without any persuasion from the experimenter, it was decided to carry out an experimental test with a series of twenty-four papers. Each animal was offered standard experimental papers, the first with a 2-in. central square, the second with a similar square but displaced to one side, the third the same but in the opposite direction, and the fourth with once again a central square.

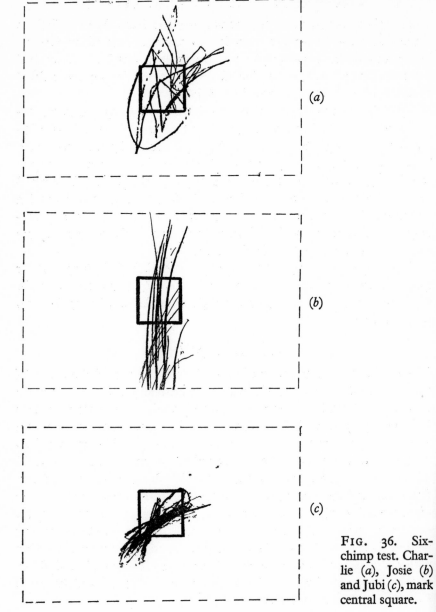

FIG. 36. Six-chimp test. Charlie (a), Josie (b) and Jubi (c), mark central square.

The whole series was obtained in one long session, each chimpanzee coming out in turn to complete its four papers. Nineteen of the twenty-four were successfully completed. One animal lost interest after three, and the sixth chimpanzee refused, as before, to take any part in the experiment whatever. The results were particularly interesting for comparative purposes and can be briefly summarized as follows:

I. JOSIE
Central squares: Confined all her markings to the region of the squares (Fig. 36b).
Offset squares: Did not mark squares; confined markings to vacant space opposite, but balance weak.

2. BEEBEE (three papers only)
Central square: Concentrated most markings in the region of the square.
Offset squares: No clear-cut results.

3. CHARLIE
Central squares: Confined his markings to the region of the squares (Fig. 36a).
Offset squares: Marked squares, but spread these markings away towards the vacant space (Fig. 37a).

4. FIFI
Central squares: Concentrated most markings in region of squares.
Offset squares: Ignored one and marked in vacant space: marked other, but then balanced it carefully (Fig. 37b).

5. JUBI
Central squares: Confined all markings to the region of the squares (Fig. 36c).
Offset squares: Concentrated most markings in the region of the squares and made no attempt to fill vacant space (Fig. 37c).

6. SAM (No response)

From these results it is obvious that once again marking a central object is more strongly expressed than balancing an off-centre figure. Ten out of the ten central-figure tests showed positive results, whereas there was only one convincing balance result from the ten offset-figure tests.

III

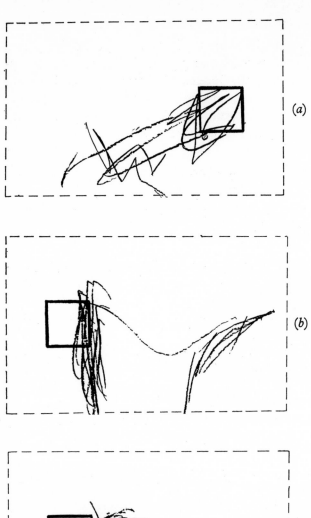

(a)

(b)

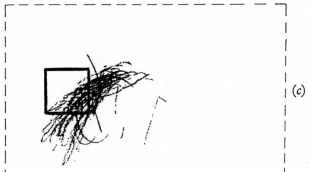

(c)

FIG. 37. Six-chimp test. Charlie (a) marks offset square. Fifi (b) marks it and then balances it. Jubi (c), like Charlie, only marks it and then fails to give balance response.

Painting by young male chimpanzee Congo, showing a subsidiary fan pattern motif. (*Collection Donald Hyden, London*)

It is interesting that, although calligraphically different from the gorilla drawings, these other chimpanzee tests show remarkable compositional similarities with the results obtained from Sophie. Once again, the degree of responsiveness in these animals is extremely encouraging and there can be little doubt that prolonged individual studies of a large group of apes would be most rewarding.

General Comparisons

The facts presented in this chapter may in many ways be rather fragmentary, but they nevertheless serve to establish beyond any doubt that there is considerable visual control exercised during picture-making by apes. Furthermore there is evidence that, where compositional factors are concerned, this control is more active and better organized in the apes than it is in the young human. This may, in part, be due to the various differences in the ways of life of the wild apes and 'wild humans'. But it is also due, in part, to the fact that the human infant is applying his mind to other problems – problems of calligraphic organization – which steal his attention away from the fundamentals of composition. Evidence from the apes to support this comes only from Congo, whose picture-making was studied long enough and known intimately enough for the experimenter to sense the gradual stifling of spatial arrangements by the step-by-step discovery of calligraphic complexities. The first discovery of a spiral, for example, is so absorbing that all attention is focused on the shape itself and its position on the page and the other blank parts of the page become so unimportant as to be non-existent. (It is for this reason – unconscious perhaps – that many modern painters have reverted to exceedingly simple shapes in order to express new compositional ideas.)

Amongst the apes, it is particularly important to note the difference between the results obtained from long periods of experimentation with Alpha and Congo and those obtained quickly from the gorilla and in the six-chimp test. In all cases there was a basic response towards the paper: the animals all showed the urge to scribble on it, to fill the space available, and to restrict themselves to the area of the paper (with the single exception of the one very young chimpanzee, Sam, who ignored the situation completely). In all cases there was a very strong tendency to mark a central figure and to restrict markings to it. But, when the question of balancing an offset figure arises, it is then that the big difference between the intensively tested animals and the quickly tested ones appears. Only with prolonged testing and complete familiarization with the experimental situation, does a chimpanzee begin to reveal the possession of the more subtle compositional capacities, such as balancing. If we had to rely only on short test studies for our information, we should undoubtedly consider the balance response as being unique to man, and it is interesting to speculate on what possible further aesthetic capabilities will be revealed when even longer and more intensive studies are carried out. Will a chimpanzee ever reach the stage of creating a pictorial image, for example? At the present stage this seems most unlikely, but I must confess that had I been asked to give an opinion concerning the possibility of a chimpanzee possessing a graphic balance response before the present study was made, I would certainly have considered it highly improbable. It is safer therefore to reserve judgement for the time being. In the meantime, however, it is possible, in the next chapter, to take a closer look at just how far the chimpanzee Congo was able to travel along the difficult path towards pictorial representation before his study was terminated.

4. Calligraphy – the Individual Units

So far the discussion has centred on the position of the lines in relation to one another, to the page, and to figures placed upon it. At this point it becomes necessary to consider the nature of the lines themselves as separate individual units.

Calligraphically, the infra-human pictures are for the most part extremely primitive. At first glance they appear to be made up of extremely simple and highly uncharacteristic short lines, with the interest lying entirely in their spatial arrangements. But a closer scrutiny reveals that whereas one chimpanzee favours short dashes another prefers long curves; where one concentrates on short, straight strokes another makes bold horizontal sweeps from left to right. Gradually it emerges that, although the lines are usually comparatively simple, they still show certain analysable characteristics.

In the case of Congo there was sufficient calligraphic change, during his two-year period of testing, to enable us to get at least a glimpse of a progression in shape and style at an infra-human level.

This type of study has never been reported before, but the comparable aesthetic growth of our own species has been carefully documented and it will be helpful to summarize first the calligraphic development that is known to take place in the human infant. It will then be possible to compare the progress Congo made with what amounts to a scale of pictorial embryology and from this comparison to judge just how far he had travelled along the path towards representational drawing.

THE KELLOGG ANALYSIS

It may be thought that the human body goes through some odd stages during its embryonic development, but the pictorial human body goes through some even odder ones as it is differentiated, month by month, by the human infant. The way in which this happens and the way in which

115

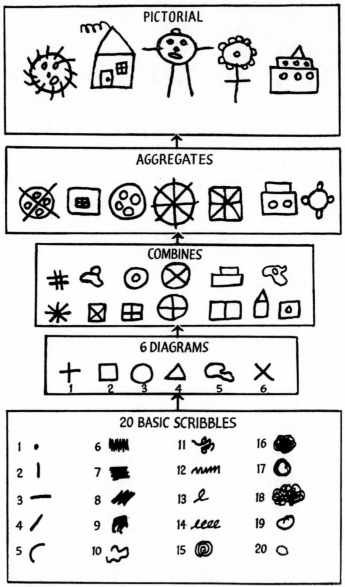

FIG. 38. Diagram by Rhoda Kellogg showing the five basic stages of calligraphic development in the human infant. (*After Kellogg, 1955.*)

pre-image scribbling develops and grows into the earliest pictorial representations has been brilliantly analysed by Rhoda Kellogg at the Golden Gate Nursery Schools, San Francisco. With the aid of an enormous sample of more than 200,000 drawings by children between the ages of two and eight, gathered from fourteen countries, she has traced human pictorial ontogeny from the crudest first attempts at marking a piece of paper, up to the point where representational objects are beginning to crystallize out into the well-known images (man, house, flower, dog) of the more familiar 'Child Art'.

The Basic Stages of Pictorial Differentiation

Kellogg recognizes five basic stages in pictorial representation (see chart in Fig. 38), as follows:

1. Scribbles.	4. Aggregates.
2. Diagrams.	5. Pictorials.
3. Combines.	

In the past, virtually all studies of child art have used stage five as the starting-point for their studies, and it is Kellogg's use of this stage as the end-point instead which has made her work so valuable and original.

She recognizes twenty basic scribble-types. These she has named as follows:

1. Dot.	11. Roving Enclosed Line.
2. Vertical Line.	12. Zigzag or Waving Line.
3. Horizontal Line.	13. Single Loop Line.
4. Diagonal Line.	14. Multiple Loop Line.
5. Curved Line.	15. Spiral Line.
6. Multiple Vertical Line.	16. Multiple Line Overlaid Circle.
7. Multiple Horizontal Line.	17. Multiple Line Circumference Circle.
8. Multiple Diagonal Line.	18. Circular Spread Out.
9. Multiple Curved Line.	19. Single Crossed Circle.
10. Roving Open Line.	20. Imperfect Circle.

These scribble-types usually start out as simple and tentative markings, then become bolder, more repetitive and more complex, until they nearly

obliterate the page. Then, apparently by a process of distillation and simplification, a new phase is reached and this is the diagram stage. Kellogg
recognizes six basic diagrams, as follows:

1. Greek Cross.   4. Triangle.
2. Square.   5. Odd Shaped Area.
3. Circle.   6. Diagonal Cross.

These diagrams arise from simple scribble combinations, such as
vertical and horizontal lines coming together to give a crude cross, or as
simplifications, from confused spiral scribbling to a pure circular shape.
The diagrams themselves advance by a process of purification, so that the
crude crossing, for example, becomes a true cross, or the circular shape
becomes a reasonable circle.

These diagrams eventually become established as fixed units and are
then themselves available to contribute to the birth of the third phase, that
of combines.

Once a vertical or Greek Cross and a diagonal cross have become
sufficiently established as distinct diagrams, for instance, it is then possible
for them to combine to produce a star shape. There are of course many
different possible combines, each one consisting of a combination of two
diagrams. When more than two diagrams are put together by the child,
then the fourth basic stage has been reached, namely the aggregate phase,
with an even greater number of possibilities.

It is the aggregate stage which, although still 'abstract' and pre-pictorial,
is of tremendous importance, as it provides the precursors for the earliest
true pictorial images.

From these aggregates there grow, slowly but surely, the various basic
pictorial clichés found in child art all over the world.

The Scribble Stage

It is useful at this point to trace these various developments, from scribbles
to pictorials, in more detail, before comparing the human scene with the
Congo material. First, there are the twenty basic scribbles.

Between the age of one and two the human infant will readily mark a sheet of paper, but its muscle co-ordinations are not mature enough for it to be able to control the situation to any great extent. The lines are usually simple, short, and often meandering. By the age of two years, the child begins to develop sufficient muscular control to perform the multiple scribblings (Nos. 6 to 9) that involve back-and-forth movements of the arm, with the pencil remaining on the surface of the paper. This type of scribble often develops next into circular spread-out (No. 16 or 18) and the page frequently becomes practically submerged under a sea of dense repetitive markings.

Gradually a distillation takes place, with simpler lines reappearing, but now with deliberate certainty and control. Unfortunately, these more advanced and specialized scribbles, such as the zigzag, the loop, and the imperfect circle, are nearly always overlaid and obscured with the dense repetitive scrawling and it requires an expert eye to distinguish them. Eventually, when the child begins to pass into the diagram stage, the over-scribbling is reduced and it disappears still more when the diagrams are being grouped together as combines or aggregates.

Very briefly, here are some of the characters of the twenty basic scribbles:

1. *The Dot.* There are several kinds, produced in different ways. They may be made by rhythmic pounding on the paper, or, alternatively, by pressing the crayon or pencil down carefully at intervals.

2. *The Straight Vertical Line.*

3. *The Straight Horizontal Line.*

4. *The Straight Diagonal Line.* These are the distilled versions of their multiple, back-and-forth forms. They also occur in a weak form in the very early pre-scribble markings of one- to two-year-olds. The vertical line is often by itself and is more common than the horizontal. The latter usually appears in combination with the vertical lines and seems to be more difficult to make. The straight diagonal line is not commonly seen by itself, although its multiple form is the most common of all child scribbles.

5. *Curved Line.* This is uncommon by itself and does not appear until towards the end of the scribble phase.

6, 7, 8 and 9. *Multiple Line Scribble.* As already explained these are

119

the first full-blooded scribbles made by infants, after sufficient development of muscle co-ordination. The diagonal multiple scribbles are the easiest to make and are most frequent.

10. *Roving Open Line.*

11. *Roving Enclosed Line.* These are meandering lines and appear in pre-scribble marking as an aimless wandering of the crayon over the sheet. When they occur later on, they do so more deliberately, as if the child were 'taking the line for a walk'. Eventually they develop into the Odd-Shaped Object, at the diagram stage.

12. *Zigzag or Waving Line.* This seems difficult to learn, but once grasped is repeated over and over again. It may develop as a kind of 'short-arc' continuous multiple scribble. It frequently appears by itself on the paper.

13. *Single Loop Line.*

14. *Multiple Loop Line.* The single loop, looking like a letter e, is rare, whereas the multiple loop line is common and often appears by itself. It plays an important role in early pictorials as smoke from a chimney or a vehicle, or as a curly tail.

15. *Spiral Line.* Only made towards the end of the scribble phase and even then is not made by all children.

16. *Multiple Line Overlaid Circle.* This commonly develops from the multiple scribbles six to nine. It may fill the paper completely.

17. *Multiple Line Circumference Circle.* This is similar to the last, but without the centre filled in. This is probably important as the precursor of the circle in the diagram stage.

18. *Circular Spread Out.* One of the most popular blotting-out techniques that often obliterate the whole page completely. This is similar to the last, but the circular movements are made with a moving arm so that there is no centre.

19. *Single Cross Circle.*

20. *Imperfect Circle.* Like number seventeen, these two scribbles are forerunners of the circle diagram. The single cross circle is simply a badly judged shape, with the line running round too far. The imperfect circle is better, but is still small and irregularly shaped.

PLATE 30. Stippled 'fan-bundle'. (*Collection Sir Julian Huxley, London.*)

PLATE 31. Stippled 'fan-bundle'. The fan itself is nearly obliterated. (*Private collection, New York.*)

PLATE 32. Stippled 'fan-bundle'. (*Collection M. S. Woods, London.*)

PLATE 33. Split fan pattern with central blob.

PLATE 34. Fan pattern with curved base. (*Collection Mrs E. Crane Chadbourne.*)

PLATE 35. Multiple-horizontal scribbling appears in later Congo
pictures, but the fan pattern persists.

PLATE 36. The use of spots occurs frequently in paintings by
Congo. (*Collection Pablo Picasso, Vauvenargues.*)

PLATE 37

PLATE 38

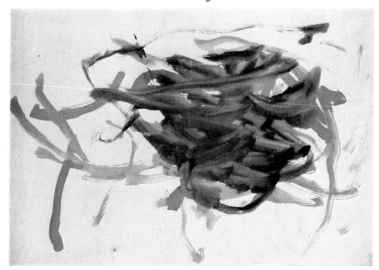

With the tachiste phase (Plate 37) contemporary art has regressed the whole way back to the multiple scribble phase of child art (Plate 38). This does not mean, however, that tachiste pictures are mere scribble for, in their regression, painters have taken with them their all knowledge of harmony, design and visual organization.

The Diagram Stage

Like the scribbles, the diagrams have an approximate sequence of appearance. The Greek Cross is the first to appear and develops from what Kellogg calls the Inherent Cross. The latter is present at the scribble stage by accident at first. Usually it first appears as a line crossing a multiple scribble, or as one multiple scribble cutting across another, but at this stage it is not yet a deliberate structure. Later, however, it appears as a simple and quite distinct crossing over of two lines and thus heralds in the diagram stage.

An interesting development out of the Greek Cross diagram is the 'multi-crossed single line', which, Kellogg reports, does not appear until after the Greek Cross has been established. This is an interesting point of difference with the ape drawings, and will be discussed later.

After the Greek Cross, there appears the Square and this is arrived at in several different ways. It may come out of double crossings, which inadvertently make a square by their intersections, or it may develop from a reaction to the sides of the paper. Kellogg notes that 'A characteristic of early scribbling is to make marks in each corner of the paper, and this happens before the crayon can be adequately controlled to enable the child to make a line around the edge'. This is intriguing in relation to Alpha's typical corner response, and it seems likely that the explanation is not as simple as it would appear at first sight.

At about the same time that the square develops, the true circle emerges from scribble precursors. Its growth is not hard to understand as it is inherently present in several of the scribble-types, as already indicated.

A little later the Odd-Shaped Area diagram appears, growing out of roving line scribbles and various other sources. This is the most common form of diagram and is recorded by Kellogg as being the easiest to make as it only requires that a line shall be joined up to itself. As we shall see later, it does not appear to be the easiest for the apes to produce.

The triangle diagram is extremely rare, so much so that it is impossible to say exactly when it first appears in relation to the other diagrams. The last diagram to appear is the diagonal cross. It is difficult to understand why this should be less frequent and appear later than the Greek Cross, particularly as the inherent crossings in the scribble stage are more frequently diagonal than Greek.

The interesting point about the growth of the diagrams is that they appear to rely for their sources almost entirely on the previous scribbles, rather than on any external environmental influences. The child's aesthetic growth appears, from Kellogg's study, to be a remarkably independent and private association between the paper, the pencil and the brain. Even at a later stage, when the early pictorial images are appearing for the first time, there appears to be only a minimum of reference to the outside world, just sufficient in fact to label the picture as a man or a house or a flower. If, for example, the earliest pictorial representations of houses by children from countries as different as Finland, Germany, India, France and Denmark are placed alongside one another it is impossible to identify them correctly, because they owe so little to the external environmental influences of the respective countries. It is, of course, this lack of external influence that makes it possible to arrive at some sort of scheme of pictorial growth, as Kellogg has done.

The Combines and Aggregates

The distinction between these two phases is only one of degree, the former being the result of a combination of two diagrams and the latter more than two. As the child progresses through these phases it comes to possess a richer and more varied visual vocabulary of shapes and arrangements, and the frequency of 'scribble-out' and 'scribble-over' is gradually reduced, so that by the time the first true pictorial representations appear, they virtually have the stage to themselves. Kellogg argues that this 'cleaning-up' process is partially brought about by parental and teacher persuasion, but, although this undoubtedly plays a part, the increasing intrinsic value and complexity of the images must also be a powerful controlling factor helping to eliminate the earlier scribble patterns.

One of the interesting facts about the combine and aggregate stages, where the child produces its most complex abstract pictures, before embarking on the long and arduous road of portrayal, is that despite the non-representational nature of the work, there are nevertheless certain forms which are strong and universal favourites, whereas there are many others that are extremely rare and are clearly not popular with children at these stages (usually at ages between three and four years).

The Kellogg study continues to analyse in detail the various popular combines and aggregates and to trace them through to the beginnings of the various fundamental pictorial images, but to discuss this at length here would take us beyond the scope of the present study. However, in order not to leave the story in mid-air, we can briefly follow through the development of one of the pictorial images (see Fig. 39). The most important one is obviously the human figure. It is also the first to appear and is one we will trace here.

The Pictorial Growth of the Human Figure

There are naturally many minor variations, from child to child, in the details of the course taken in getting from the first scribble to the first drawing of a human form. But despite this, the overall trend is so uniform that it is possible to give a very clear picture of this development by taking one imaginary average child and following it through a typical sequence:

The first pictures this imaginary child makes consist of weak wandering lines. This occurs at the age of one, but a year later the infant has mastered multiple back and forth movements and is making bold scribblings. These develop into horizontal loopings, then into spirallings and finally into confused multiple circlings. The circling movement becomes a satisfying one and is purified and simplified until, at the age of three, the child is producing its first circles. Now that they are produced in a pure form, the circles look empty and the child begins to fill them up with spots and dashes. This gives rise to the idea of crossing out the circle and the child draws bold lines across it, this way and that. While all this has been going on the child has also learnt to make crosses and to combine crosses to make a star shape. When the circle is being crossed out, the star shape turns out to be a perfect fit and can be used to make a satisfyingly symmetrical pattern. This double cross inside a circle gives a basic aggregate of Mandala

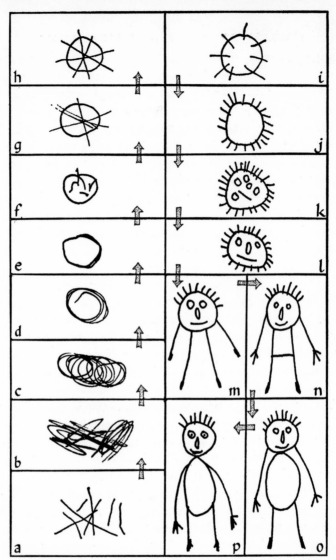

FIG. 39. Schematic representation of typical phases in the graphical differentiation of the human figure. (a) Simple scribble lines. (b) Multiple scribble. (c) Circular multiple scribble. (d) Simplified circular scribbling. (e) Circle. (f) Marks inside circle (this is as far as Congo was able to proceed along this differentiation path). (g) Circle crossed with lines. (h) 'Mandala' stage. (i) Mandala with empty centre. (j) 'Sunburst' stage. (k) Marked sunburst. (l) First representation – a face. (m) 'Cephalopod' stage, with four rays extended as arms and legs. (n) Head-plus-body stage. (o) Body becomes distinct from head. (p) Arms shift to correct position, from head to trunk. (*Partly after Kellogg, 1955.*)

design. Kellogg considers this to be the most important unit of pre-representational drawing. Its occurrence is universal and frequent and it appears to be vital for the stages that are to follow.

Gradually a modified Mandala pattern, which has been called the Sunburst pattern (not by children, but by experimenters), grows out of the double-crossed circle by the reduction and loss of the cross lines inside the circle and an extension of them outside it. This gives the appearance of a sun with rays coming from it. The empty central space now demands to be filled up again and this is done with spots and small circles. When, by chance, as Kellogg says, 'the inner circles are four in number and they occur in a "face" formation, the face looks out at the child, and he seems to be as surprised to see it as is the bystanding adult'. This is the great moment of pictorial creation and, like all the other previous stages of development, it has come to the child as a pleasant discovery, growing naturally out of a gradual calligraphic process, rather than from some sudden input from the external world. With previous, non-representational drawings, the child will often have been asked by insensitive adults 'What are you drawing?', or 'What is it supposed to be?' and, with a child's ingenuity, will have answered that it is 'Daddy', or 'My house', or whatever sprung immediately to mind. This does not mean that there was any *a priori* selection of image for the drawing, but is simply a method of getting rid of unwanted interference as quickly as possible. But once the child has discovered the formula for producing an image which immediately strikes him as being representative of something, then a new phase has begun.

With the face identified as a face, it might be supposed that the rest of the human figure will quickly follow, but this is not the case. The face problem may have been solved, but not the body, or the legs, or the fingers, or any of the other details. These must grow naturally and slowly, just as the previous stages grew.

The rays of what was the sunburst pattern have now become magically transformed into hair. The rays on top of the head are often increased in number and those underneath the head are reduced. The latter often become longer and then by a very small step become arms and legs. Once again the secret of the development is the taking of small natural steps, rather than bold jumps.

The figure now portrayed is often referred to (again, by experimenters, not children) as a Cephalopod, because both the arms and the legs come out of what appears to be the head. Actually this is misleading, for, although it is a convenient term for describing a highly characteristic stage, it is not true to say that the circular shape is the head alone. It is the as yet undifferentiated human form and only appears to be the head alone because the face happens to fill its surface. The next stage is, indeed, the separation of head and body into two discrete units. This is sometimes done by a sort of cell division, but more typically by the drawing of a single line across between the legs. There is now a head and a body, but no neck and the next step is the making of a constriction in the appropriate region. At this moment the child is apparently unaware of the fact that the arms have been left high and dry, sticking out of the head. So powerful is the head shape, with its ancient origins, stretching back into the distant scribble stage, that it still holds the arms firm and it is some time before they shift down to take up their proper place at the top of the body.

Basically the human figure is now pictorially formed. While these developments have been going on there will undoubtedly have been a certain amount of minor experimentation with ears and teeth and toes and fingers, but these developments vary considerably in their exact sequences of appearance.

From this point on the child will *set out to draw* a human figure, rather than happen on it, and gradually the demands of objective representation will suppress the more natural obedience to the abstract laws of differentiation, which have helped to form the image out of scribble and scrawl. This process will take ten years or more and this is not the place to pursue it further.

The child, who is probably now between four and five years old, will have to start copying things from the external world, instead of drawing on its private graphic experience. This copying technique will be something new and unfamiliar, something which must be welded on to what has gone before, and it will take time. In typical cases it takes over ten years and during this time child pictures become more and more ugly until, the uncomfortable pupation over, they emerge into adult forms. What happens next will be discussed in the final chapter.

CONGO CALLIGRAPHY

With this résumé of the human scene, it is now possible to take a look at the calligraphic achievements of Congo, such as they are, and see just how far along the path of differentiation they go. It need hardly be said that no ape has yet reached the stage of pictorial representation, but it will emerge from the following that Congo came tantalizingly near to it. Whether the infra-human brain will ever be capable of reaching that stage is still an open question and, although most unlikely, cannot be completely ruled out.

Congo Scribble-types

Congo's earlier pictures were made up of simple, straight, or slightly bent lines, with little or no calligraphic interest. This state of affairs persisted for some time, although dramatic improvements were being made in the meantime as far as his line arrangements or compositions were concerned. The fact that he was able during this phase to make careful and sensitive compositional modifications points immediately to a fundamental difference between his picture-making and that of the human infants at this early stage.

Congo was not yet ready to make back-and-forth multiple scribbles of the type which develop in human infants at the age of two. Kellogg has referred to this pre-multiple-scribble stage as a phase of immature muscle co-ordination, where the simple lines produced have little value or meaning, as the child lacks real control over what it is doing. The situation with young apes is very different, for their muscular development at this graphic stage is comparatively far advanced. This is, of course, due to the fact that the apes are tree-dwellers and the human beings are not. The young chimpanzee must have strong arms to cling to its mother and to swing through the branches and its muscle development is quite capable of dealing with a simple problem like gripping a pencil and moving it steadily this way and that under visual guidance. This means that the young ape could be expected to start straight away with multiple scribbling. The fact that it does not do so means that it is necessary to consider afresh the interpretation of the early human responses. I do not doubt that the muscular co-ordination is insufficiently advanced to produce the more elaborate multiple scribbling, but what does seem to be in doubt now is whether the child would draw in this way, even if it did have a more developed muscular system. What this means is that the very first 'pre-scribble' phase in human picture-making is probably a genuine phase, which is calligraphically distinct from the later bold-scribbling stage, independently of any muscular changes.

This is a somewhat theoretical point as far as human studies are concerned, but it is most important to realize that the 'weak-muscle-criticism' of the one- to two-year-old human infant products must not be automatically applied to the analysis of early ape calligraphy. It is probably better for comparative purposes to consider the scribble stage as having three distinct phases in both instances:

Phase A: Primary simple lines (well controlled in apes, poorly controlled in man).

Phase B: Multiple scribbling and spread-outs.

Phase C: Secondary simplification, but with greater variety of detailed line shape, leading to diagrams.

Looking now at these phases in Congo, we find the following types of basic scribble present:

1. *Dots*: Were produced in two ways. Like human infants, Congo made them either by rapid rhythmic pounding with a vertically held brush, crayon, or pencil, or he applied them gently and laboriously as check marks. The former type occurred at very low intensities (judged by distraction responses and uneasy body movements) either at the beginning of a picture, before it had captured his attention, or at the end, when he had exhausted his interest in the page in question. The result of this type of dotting can be seen in the bold stippling over the fan-bundle in Plate 31 and in the simple but strikingly balanced picture in Plate 36. It is worthy of note that, despite the low intensity and the rapid delivery of

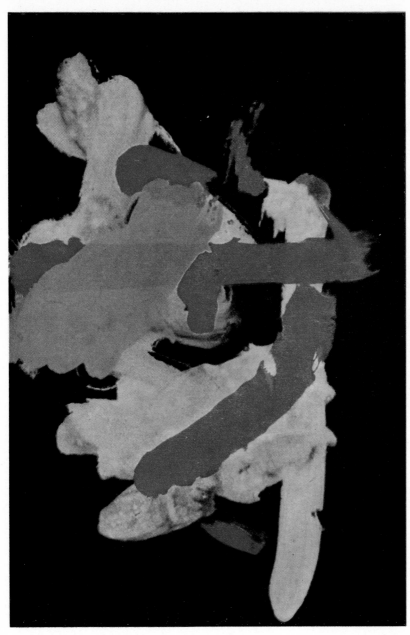

PLATE K. Simple painting by Congo showing the use of vertical, horizontal and diagonal lines.

the strokes, the dots were nevertheless under visual control in most cases and did not pile up on one another, but were spread out rather evenly. The second type of spotting is seen in the experimental drawings in Figs. 17a and 19c, for example. Here the marks are gentle and performed with very high intensity concentration. Dotting of this kind was almost always confined to check marks on experimental figures, or to corner-marking.

   2. *Vertical Line.*
   3. *Horizontal Line.*
   4. *Diagonal Line.* These appeared frequently (see Plate K) and made up the greater part of all Congo's earlier work. The vertical and diagonal lines were the most common and occurred, for example, in all of the ninety fan-pattern drawings. Horizontal lines appeared less often and, as with the human infants, appeared to be more difficult to make. They appeared in later fan patterns as extreme side-pieces in fans with an arc of 180 degrees. They also appeared as part of the base of bundles in fan-bundles. Unlike the comparable human lines, the vertical, horizontal and diagonal lines made by Congo existed in bold, accurate forms *before* the onset of multiple scribbling as well as after it.

   5. *Curved Line.* This appeared extremely frequently (see Fig. 40) and often merged with types two, three, and four. I suspect that the more powerful arm muscles of the chimpanzee account for the fact that this type of line is less common in children.

   6, 7, 8 and 9. *Multiple Line Scribble:* Congo was one and a half years old when he started to draw. He was nearly two and a half before the first multiple scribbles appeared and even then they did not appear very frequently. But by the time he was three, they were beginning to dominate the scene more and more until towards the end of his test period, Congo was either making bold multiple onslaughts (Fig. 41) or investigating new and subtle shapes. Even the rare fan patterns that he fell back on from time to time were now made up of complex loops. All the four types of multiple scribble were quite common.

   10. *Roving Open Line.*
   11. *Roving Enclosed Line.* These two appeared from time to time, but

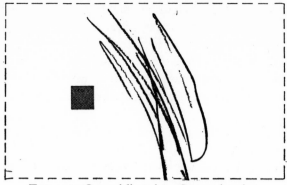

FIG. 40. Curved lines in a Congo drawing.

FIG. 41. Multiple scribbling by Congo.

were not common. Congo put such energy and purpose into his drawing that anything meandering was somehow out of character. Only when presented with a pencil or crayon with an unfamiliar texture was he prone to meander. This occurred particularly with a very soft pencil on smooth paper (Fig. 42).

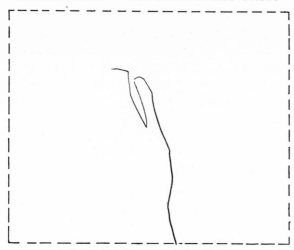

FIG. 42. Congo – roving line.

12. *Zigzag or Waving Line.* Extremely rare in Congo. The first genuine zigzag did not appear until after a year and a half of drawing and painting. As in human drawings, it seemed to be difficult to learn, but satisfying once achieved. A further similarity was that it appeared first as an abbreviated form of multiple scribbling and then quickly became simplified (Fig. 43).

FIG. 43. Zig-zag lines were rare in Congo's work and only occurred, as here, in his later phases.

13. *Single Loop Line.*

14. *Multiple Loop Line.* Here the ape and the human differed. The human rarely made a single loop but frequently made multiple loopings. With Congo the reverse occurred, the single loop being a brilliantly executed favourite of Congo's, after about one year of drawing (see Plate L). The multiple loop line only appeared towards the end of the two-year period.

15. *Spiral Line.* As with children, this was rare and only appeared on a few occasions when drawing was at very high intensity.

16. *Multiple Line Overlaid Circle.*

17. *Multiple Line Circumference Circle.* As with children, this developed gradually out of multiple horizontal scribbling. Many examples show an intermediate form, which is oval in shape (Plate M). The circumference form is, of course, only a matter of degree and in a few cases Congo was seen to reach this point, but never left the result alone, always either obliterating it or filling it in.

18. *Circular Spread Out.* This was rare in Congo, but would probably have been more common, had it been possible to continue testing, because several examples of it appeared in his last session. (see Fig. 44).

19. *Single Crossed Line.*

20. *Imperfect Circle.* It is difficult to distinguish between these two types, except where the shape is left untouched and un-embellished. Unfortunately, Congo made a number of circular shapes during his later sessions, but nearly always covered them over. In order to preserve one of these circles (Fig. 45), the card was snatched away on one occasion, when the circle was the first shape drawn. As with the human infants, these shapes were only drawn in Phase C of the scribble stage, after the multiple scribbling had been fully expressed, and it is likely that here too there was a development by simplification and distillation.

From this list it is clear that in many ways, Congo and the human children had very similar scribble responses. It seems likely that the differences between them at this stage were due to the differences in muscular development, rather than to any differences in mental processes. The fact that Congo was composing his pictures in a better way during his

FIG. 44. Spread-out obliteration occurring towards the end of Congo's painting period.

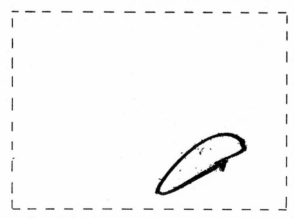

FIG. 45. Imperfect circle obtained from Congo by snatching the card away from him before he obliterated it.

earlier phases is undoubtedly due to the same muscular differences. For, by the time the children have sufficient control over their pencils, their brains are already at that stage which is dominated by calligraphic variation and invention.

Congo Diagrams

Already, at the diagram stage, the ape begins to lag behind. Only two of the six diagrams are achieved with any degree of certainty: the circle and the cross. In both these cases there are peculiar extensions beyond the simple diagrams, which are most unexpected, but with the other four types of diagram, there is but a vague precursor to indicate what might have been.

1. *The Greek Cross.* It will be recalled that Alpha showed a tendency to cross pre-prepared lines, but that Congo showed this response only once (Fig. 24a). This nevertheless proved that he was capable of such a reaction, even if it was rarely called forth, for the repeated crossing of the vertical line on that one occasion was far too deliberate to have been accidental. In later non-experimental drawings, however, Congo did show three types of crossing, without any test figures having been placed on the paper. The first type was seen in multiple scribbling, where a bold marking back and forth in one direction would sometimes be ended with a single savage line running clear across this scribble at right angles to it. This type

FIG. 46. Star-like crossing by Congo, a rare but deliberately formed pattern.

FIG. 47. *Multiple crossing of a single self-made line. One of Congo's most advanced patterns. (Detail copied from more complex drawing.)*

is common in human infants also, according to Kellogg. The second type was rare and consisted of a confused starlike shape, with a definite centre point and lines radiating from it, with the emphasis on side-to-side and up-and-down lines, so that the result was rather like a series of crosses drawn inaccurately on top of one another (Fig. 46). The third type was the most remarkable and really goes beyond the simple diagram stage. This was quite deliberate multiple crossing of a single self-made line. It was carried out with tremendous concentration and extreme care and, although rarely seen, was unmistakable (Fig. 47). Now, according to Kellogg, this figure appears only after the pure cross has been mastered, but Congo never to my knowledge reached the stage of a pure cross, but jumped from cross-precursors, straight to multi-crossed lines. Unfortunately, he usually destroyed the latter with over-scribbling.

2. *The Square.* Congo never achieved a true square. He made many accidentally by scoring horizontal multiples across repeated verticals, but these chance squares were never taken up as clues to further developments.

3. *The Circle.* Towards the end of his painting career, Congo was producing excellent circles, but nearly always filled them in immediately. Luckily he was filmed at this stage and the careful formation of a pure circle can be witnessed, followed immediately by a precise filling in of its centre and then finally an overall obliteration. Apart from the one imperfect circle referred to in the last section, it was possible to save only one good example and this is most unusual because, like the crossing, it

135

FIG. 48. The most advanced stage of differentiation yet produced by any infra-human picture-maker. Congo made his own circle and then procedeed to mark inside it. In human infants this is the precursor stage to the first representational pictures of faces.

goes farther than the simple diagram (Fig. 48). It consists of a carefully drawn circle, made in chalk in the centre of a large sheet, with several small marks inside it. It is, in fact, exactly equivalent to stage f in the diagram in which I have shown, schematically, the development of the human figure from early scribbling (Fig. 39). In other words, it is one step nearer to the creation of a face than an ordinary circle. It almost reaches the

FIG. 49. Earliest representation of a face, by a human infant. Note the great similarity between this and Congo's drawing in Fig. 48.

stage of a combine, with a cross inside a circle and undoubtedly represents the highest degree of calligraphic differentiation yet achieved by any infra-human individual. It was created, like the multi-crossed lines, with intense concentration. Despite the fact that the animal was at a late stage in the two-year period and was becoming extremely 'physical', the creation of a marked circle so fascinated him that he became almost human in his self-control. As soon as the picture was complete, he relaxed and became his usual extrovert self again. Similar changes were observed on one or two

137

occasions when Congo was set extremely difficult, but very novel, intelligence tests. It was particularly tantalizing that it was not possible to pursue the drawing tests further with Congo. If more detailed experiments are attempted in the future, the administration of tranquilizers, or drugs that reduce bodily activity but which do not reduce test responsiveness, may prove immensely valuable in extending this process of graphic differentiation still further.

4. *The Triangle.* Only once did Congo show a pattern which could be described as a triangular shape, and that is very much of a precursor (Fig. 50). It will be recalled that this diagram was also rare among children.

5. *Odd-Shaped Area.* Although common with children, this did not appear in Congo's work in a clear-cut form.

6. *Diagonal Cross.* Congo's precursor crosses were basically made up of horizontal and vertical lines, but were not particularly accurate. His multi-crossed lines consisted of one long line with short lines crossing it at right angles. The diagonal cross is not therefore established with any certainty.

From this list of comments on Congo's achievements in the realm of diagrams, it is clear that this is the region which now requires special study in the future. The scribble stage is clearly extremely similar to that found in our own species but it is here, with the diagrams, that the paths of

FIG. 50. The only example of a triangular shape produced by Congo.

ape and man begin to diverge, and it is here therefore that every scrap of additional evidence will be valuable.

CALLIGRAPHY OF OTHER APES

Unfortunately the calligraphic information from other ape sources is very meagre. Most individuals show dots, vertical lines, horizontal lines, diagonal lines and curved lines. Some show multiple scribbles. But the more subtle scribble-types are missing. This is, of course, what one would expect, considering the small samples in most cases and the length of time it took to arrive at interesting results with Congo. There are a few special points of interest, however.

During the 'six-chimp' test it was noticed that after only a few trials, it was possible to identify each of the animals by their style of drawing. This style was not a compositional, but a calligraphic matter. The lines were not categorically different, but were drawn in a slightly different way in each case, sufficient to give each animal a style of its own. An even more marked case was that of Jonny, the adult male chimpanzee at the Vienna Zoo. For some months I had only one example of his work (Fig. 3) and this was so strange that I was sure it must be atypical. It comprised a mass of tiny, brief, meandering lines, faintly and nervously drawn and scattered all over the page with a complete absence of any organization. When a photograph of a similar style was sent to me I knew, without even looking at the caption, that this was another example of Jonny's work and that the first one had not been atypical after all.

Another stylistic shock arrived with the first adult gorilla drawings from Sophie. Instead of great massive strokes boldly covering the page, each drawing was made up of minute zigzags. Once again there was virtually no spatial organization, except the basic response of keeping to the area of the page. As can be seen from Plate 10 and Figs. 32, 33 and 34, there can be no mistaking the calligraphy of Sophie.

As already discussed, Alpha showed the crossing response. So, too, did Joni, the Russian chimpanzee, who clearly reveals another case of multicrossed lines in Fig. 1c.

Alpha also shows an interesting difference between her early and her late scribbles. In her first drawings she shows short, timid markings and later develops to the bold multiple scribbles, as did Congo. But Alpha was fully adult, even when the tests were started, so here is further proof that the simplicity of early drawings is not necessarily due to immature muscle co-ordination. It is also worth recalling that Alpha, after a rest of fifteen months, during which she made no drawings, reverted to her earlier style. Contrasting with this is evidence from the 'six-chimp' test, where one of the animals (Fifi) sat down and produced bold and elaborate drawings (Fig. 8) at her very first session. Also, Zippy, the New York chimpanzee, with little experience nevertheless started out straight away with pre-dominantly horizontal motifs (Plates 12 and 13), as did Alexander, the London Zoo orang-utan (Plates A and B).

The evidence is clearly conflicting over this question and, although it is evident that each ape has its own particular style, sufficiently distinct for its pictures to be identified in a mixed collection, it is not at all certain what determines the 'starting style' when one of these animals is faced with pencil and paper for the first time.

5. Conclusion—the Biology of Art

Having examined the ape material in detail it is now possible to establish just how far it can help us in understanding human art as a biological, or behavioural, phenomenon. The ape pictures are, of course, interesting enough in their own right and need no further justification, but certain intriguing relationships between ape picture-maker and human artist have already inevitably emerged and it is obviously worth pursuing this comparison farther. But first, here is a brief summary of the ape facts.

Recapitulation

During the past fifty years thirty-two infra-human primates have produced drawings and paintings. Of these, twenty-three were chimpanzees, two were gorillas, three were orang-utans, and four were capuchin monkeys. In all cases the animals received no assistance or guidance from the experimenters, except for the provision of and, in the first instance, familiarization with the drawing or painting equipment. Attempts to influence the kind of picture produced by provoking imitative responses were always most unsuccessful.

Few if any of the thirty-two animals received any reward for picture-making, and the response was not only self-rewarding, but extremely powerful in many cases. Two of the chimpanzees, Alpha and Congo, were studied intensively, the former producing over 200 pictures and the latter nearly 400. Similarities between these two included (1) a tendency to fill a blank page, but not to scribble outside it, (2) a tendency to mark a central figure, (3) a tendency to balance an offset figure, (4) a tendency to become calligraphically bolder as time went on, starting with simple lines and changing more and more to multiple scribbles.

In the case of one chimpanzee, Congo, the calligraphic growth of his patterns took him as far along the human developmental path as the 'diagram stage', with the production of complete circles. In addition, several chimpanzees showing a crossing or intersection response.

Owing to the advanced muscular development of the young chimpanzee, the early scribbles, produced before any calligraphic developments have occurred, are sufficiently controlled to enable the animals to make reasonably precise compositional responses. The human infant's pictures at a comparable stage are too inaccurate for this and later, when the muscle co-ordination is sufficiently developed, the brain of the child has developed to the point where the interest is dominated by the absorbing problems of calligraphic differentiation.

This process of pictorial differentiation takes approximately ten years in the human being. It is therefore preferable to carry out tests that are designed to analyse the fundamentals of visual composition with chimpanzees rather than with human children. On the other hand, no ape, no matter how old or experienced, has yet been able to develop graphically to the pictorial stage of simple representation. The study of the birth and growth of imagery must therefore be made with human infants rather than apes (the most vital years being between two and five).

Adult Picture-makers

Differences in the relationship between the rates of muscular and mental growth and development in terrestrial man and arboreal apes may help to explain much of the difference that can be seen in pictures made by very young apes and very young humans. It cannot explain, however, the even more striking differences between the picture-making results of adult apes and those of adult humans. Here, with individuals of both species enjoying full muscular development, there are obviously other major factors at work.

To say that these adult differences are the outcome of the evolution in man of a more elaborate brain structure is too facile an answer. The brain differences are of course vital, but causally they have only an indirect bearing on the case. They occurred in connexion with a major ecological and sociological change and it is only by examining this change as a whole that we can hope to find a more revealing answer to the problem.

The familiar evolutionary picture of man's ancestry depicts a group of primates becoming too heavy to hop or run along branches, switching subsequently to a hanging and swinging form of locomotion termed brachiation, and losing their then obsolete tails. With this body form, some of man's ancestors are then visualized descending from the tropical forests to the open plains where, adapting to the comparative lack of their basic fruit diet, they took to hunting in groups. From this type the genus *Homo* arose. Other types stayed put in the trees, such as the ancestors of the gibbons and the orang-utans, while the forerunners of the chimpanzees and the gorillas found a compromise both in structure and behaviour.

Only the more terrestrial ancestral groups would have had the front legs totally emancipated from the chore of locomotion and freed for purely manipulative actions. At this point the birth of tool-making became possible, and reasonably precise weapons could be fashioned. It is true that the great apes, and certain monkeys too, throw stones and sticks at their enemies with a remarkably accurate aim, but the hands of these species are still required as aids to locomotion and it is argued that it was only with the hunting, ground-living, genus *Homo* that the creation of more precise weapons was possible. From weapons to more complex implements of all kinds was a comparatively small step and it was not long before man was scratching and painting pictures on the ground, on rocks, in caves, on animal skins, or on trees.

We have no records to show exactly when this last phase, the phase of picture-making, began. From the period dating 250,000 years ago up to about 30,000 to 40,000 years ago, a closely related species, Neanderthal Man, dominated the scene. He was a tool-making species who also made fire, carried out burial ceremonies and who almost certainly possessed some sort of simple speech. Despite these undoubted assets he was a total failure and was completely obliterated when Modern Man came on the scene with more advanced implements. Within ten thousand years of his arrival this new species, *Homo sapiens*, had produced the cave paintings at Lascaux and Altamira. Obviously these were not his first fumbling attempts but mature expressions of an advanced picture-making culture, the origins of which appear to be lost to us for ever.

THE BIOLOGY OF ART

This, then, is the generally accepted story, but from a study of the previous chapters of this book it will probably occur to the reader that if the emancipation of the hands was such a vital link in the chain of events that led eventually to the origin of human picture-making, it is strange that apes today can be persuaded to reveal such a strong, hidden potential for painting and drawing and do not seem to suffer from any greater manipulative difficulties than human children. Furthermore, if they have these easily provoked responses available to them, why have they not been utilized further, as they were by man?

The answer to why apes, both young and adult, can become engrossed in picture-making to the point where, as we have seen, they may prefer it to being fed and will exhibit temper-tantrums if they are stopped, is a difficult one to find. It has something to do with the great development in apes, especially chimpanzees, of what I have called 'Self-Rewarding Activities'. These are actions which, unlike most patterns of animal behaviour, are performed for their own sake rather than to attain some basic biological goal. They are 'activities for activities' sake', so to speak. They normally occur in animals which have all their survival problems under control and have surplus nervous energy which seems to require an outlet. This usually only occurs in young animals whose needs are being looked after by their parents, or in captive or domestic animals whose needs are attended to by their human owners. Actions which are usually referred to as play, curiosity, self-expression, investigation, and so forth, come into this category of self-rewarding activities. Most of them are basically physical, motoric outbursts and are fundamentally similar to human gymnastics and sports, except that they lack any ulterior motives such as the obtaining of health, money, or social standing. They may inadvertently keep the animal mentally and physically healthy and thus indirectly assist it in its struggle for survival, but the actual driving force behind these self-rewarding activities appears to be simply the unleashing of surplus nervous energy. In this connexion it is noticeable that it is just those species which are particularly active when they are faced with life's usual survival problems, that are also especially prone to perform self-rewarding activities when everything is taken care of for them. Those species

PLATE L

Congo painting with bold circular loop.

Multiple circling in one of Congo's last paintings.

which have solved the problem of survival by adopting a waiting, watching, stealthy mode of existence – snakes for example – are the ones which are least likely ever to show playful outbursts, or indulge in light-hearted games.

Self-rewarding activities are not always gymnastic and it is amongst the primates and especially the great apes that we find manipulative investigation taken to a striking extreme in captive specimens. Any strange objects will be investigated, opened, closed, moved, shaken, rearranged, pulled, pushed, stretched, twisted and generally thoroughly examined. These investigations are often rhythmically performed, as are the gymnastics. Objects may be tapped rhythmically, or moved about in a repetitive pattern of actions, in a fundamentally similar way to the rhythmic 'dancing' performances carried out during the physical gymnastic outbursts.

This spatial adjustment of objects and the regular appearance of rhythmic repetition in self-rewarding activities is obviously of basic importance in relation to picture-making. The stage is set, as it were, for rhythmic, spatially organized responses which, if given the appropriate equipment, will lead naturally to the first pictures. With gymnastic invention, chimpanzees soon tire of one type of action and shift to another one, constantly varying their rhythmic movement 'themes', and the same principle applies to picture-making. Luckily there is sufficient interest within the subject itself to permit these variations to exist from picture to picture. If this were not the case, picture-making as a whole would quickly be replaced by some totally different activity. The more the animals come to vary their graphic responses, the more visual control they must exert and in this way it is possible for a chimpanzee such as Congo to progress through phase after phase.

But it has been stressed that all this goes on only when the animals are being 'taken care of' in one way or another and, in the wild, this means that only the young apes would be inclined to behave in this way. They might well scratch marks in the earth or on the trees from time to time, but with the advent of adulthood such things would be swept aside and forgotten in the face of the more immediate problems of survival.

This takes us back to the second question, namely why, if they have a strong picture-making potential, have the apes not developed and utilized it as adults in the wild. It may seem that that question has just been answered, but, all else being equal, prehistoric man might reasonably also have been expected to show these responses in infancy and then also let them fade out as he became adult. But all else was not equal and the differences in his way of life, from that led by the great apes, gives us the clue as to the way in which human picture-making did in fact cling on into adult life and eventually become a vital part of it.

The situation was probably as follows. The apes, living in small no-madic bands, feeding on an abundance of fruits and berries in the forest regions, would have little need of advanced forms of communication. Even the chimpanzee, the noisiest of the apes, has only a limited vocabu-lary of grunts and screams and can communicate no more than its basic moods such as fear, anger, contentment, hunger, panic and so on. The ground-living ancestors of the *Homo* group, however, hunters by recent adaptation rather than by ancient specialization, with no structural modifications to teeth or nails to aid them, must have found feeding by hunting and killing an arduous task. Their ancestoral hatred of small moving objects such as snakes and spiders (seen also in the apes of today) was there to equip them with a killer's 'vicious streak', and the lack of the usual forest food was there to give them the necessary hunger motivation. But, only by developing good weapons and by banding together as a hunting group could success be assured. Group attack can be observed in primates today in respect of a common enemy and this response probably required little adjustment to shift it from a reaction to being attacked, to one in which the group was the attacker. But hunting and the passing on of information about hunting techniques must have required a much more elaborate communication system than anything possessed by man's ancestors. Unlike the 'professional' killers of the carnivore world, man had to use co-operative planning if he was to be really successful on the hunt. As soon as he had a real language which described objects as well as moods, the gateway was open to the pictorial representation of these objects.

It is at this point that so-called prehistoric art comes on the scene and

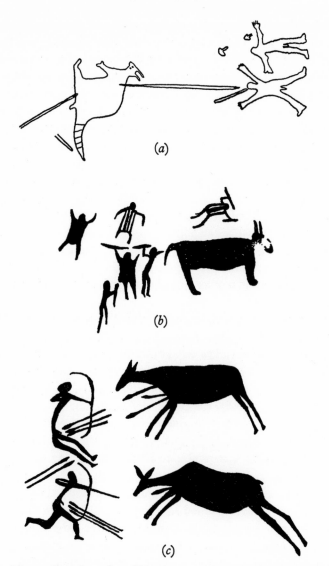

(a)

(b)

(c)

FIG. 51. The uniformity of prehistoric art. These hunting scenes from (a)
Australia, (b) Asia, and (c) Europe are remarkably alike in subject matter, all de-
picting the vital man-weapon-animal relationship.

147

does so for one or both of two reasons. Firstly, there is the utilitarian reason, namely hunting description and instruction. Nearly all prehistoric art depicts hunted species or actual hunting scenes (Fig. 51). Secondly there is the religious reason. It has been widely suggested that the painting of symbolic animals was thought to assist, by a process of sympathetic magic, in the domination of the real animals themselves, and there is a great deal of comparative anthropological evidence to support this view.

Which of these two reasons was more important at the various stages of prehistoric development is a matter for much debate. It seems likely, for example, that the more strictly utilitarian pictures were ones which were scratched in the sand or in some other simple way and that have since been lost to us for ever. The famous cave paintings, however, being so inaccessible were more probably religious or magical in significance. One thing, anyway, is clear, namely that neither instruction nor magical aids are required where survival depends on fruit-gathering, and the forest-dwelling apes could have had neither stimulus towards bigger and better picture-making.

It is not suggested, however, that our picture-making hunter-ancestors were purely concerned with producing utilitarian diagrams or religious symbols. Very crude sketches will suffice for either. But anyone who has walked through the new entrance of the caves at Lascaux and has stood staring open-mouthed at the pictures on their walls, will be aware that an extra element was present – the element of aesthetics.

It is significant that it is this aesthetic aspect of picture-making that man shares with the apes and which led to the extraordinary situation in which two chimpanzees were able to hold an exhibition of paintings in a London art gallery. For, as we have seen, both men *and* apes possess a sense of design and composition although, as already stated, it was only man the hunter whose needs led him to utilize this talent and so develop picture-making as an active part of his natural existence. But having developed it to such an enormous degree during his history, how can it have come about that such simple pictures as those shown in this book are of sufficient interest today to be shown in an art gallery? To understand this we must pass on from prehistoric to historic times.

The Rise and Fall of Representational Art

We have seen that man the hunter indulged in picture-making with a triple motivation, the pictures being, at the same or different times, magico-religious, utilitarian, and/or aesthetic. The element of utilitarian communication, either by the transmission of messages from a distance, or by immediate visual description and instruction, or by the keeping of records, was an aspect of picture-making that was bound to develop and expand as man's social structure developed and became more complex.

The great step which man took, when he waved farewell to his nomadic ancestry and settled down to become an agricultural species, took him also over another vital threshold, namely from picture-making to writing. As hunting gave way to farming and storing and trading, so the need for the keeping of records grew and with it grew more and more efficient recording techniques. As soon as writing had developed fully to cope with this new problem, picture-making lost one of its major functions. However, although it may have been pushed into second place as a communication system, its aesthetic and magico-religious values remained comparatively unchanged.

From this point, approximately five thousand years ago, up to the present day, there are then two parallel lines of development. Along one, we see the gradual increase, hand in hand, of the complexity of our social structures and the efficiency of our communication techniques. Along the other we see the gradual dwindling of the importance of picture-making as even a second-place communication system and also, eventually, in the religious field.

The main events in this story are well known. The advent of printing gave a major boost to writing, but it was not until very recent times that picture-making received its biggest blow. For, up to the latter part of the last century, it was still possible to argue that no *words* could record certain events or persons as clearly as good pictures. Ever since the written word had replaced the pictorial symbol, art had become increasingly representational, even to the extreme lengths of mimicking three dimensions on the flat surfaces. It was its only hope, and detailed, accurate visual representation its only stronghold. But then, with the advent of automatic picture-making by a chemical process which came to be called photography, this communication value was swept away also.

With the perfection of photographic techniques, including the addition of colour processes and cinematography accompanied by various sound recording methods, culminating today in such electronic sound and vision techniques as colour video-tape, blow fell upon blow.

As if this were not enough, the religious element in picture-making motivation, which had stood it in good stead during historic times, also dwindled away as religion gradually lost its grip on the increasingly complex human societies.

The situation at the present time therefore is one in which picture-making plays only a minor role in the fields of religion and utilitarian communication, but still retains, untouched and untrammelled, its major role in the field of pure aesthetics.

So today picture-making has turned full cycle and is back almost where it began before ape-man became man-hunter. Now, at last the ape and the modern man have much the same interest in producing pictures, and it might even be argued that the modern human artist has little more reason for painting a picture than does a chimpanzee. As we have seen, the outcome of this is that contemporary human picture-makers and ape picture-makers produce startlingly similar results. This does not imply that these results are *exactly* similar, or that the human pictures are bad. They are the inevitable outcome of the dwindling strength of all but the aesthetic motivation in the painter and, since this is the vital element that separates art from document, they should be accepted for what they are – pure forms of artistic expression.

However, in order to balance these statements, it should also be stressed that the addition to a picture of a communicative representational image, either diagrammatic or precise, does not harm or reduce the aesthetic value of the visual production in any way. In other words, not only is it impossible to say that the 'pure' pictures of contemporary art are *worse* (aesthetically) than their representational forerunners, but it is also equally true to say that they are not, of necessity, any better. They simply omit the communication element which has been taken over by the more efficient photographic and electronic techniques.

We have seen that the reason why apes have not taken their potential aesthetic talents further and put them into practice was clearly because they had no reason for doing so, beyond aesthetic pleasure. It now emerges that man is in a similar position today and yet he still persists with his picture-making activities. But the reason is not hard to find. He has had a long and glorious tradition of picture-making behind him and all the necessary materials are available to him. Both man and the apes have an in-herent need to express themselves aesthetically and, given painting materials, will respond in a basically similar fashion. Without these materials, chimpanzees express themselves, as discussed earlier, by other more gymnastic means, which contain aesthetic rhythms and patterns in just the same way.

The Contemporary Scene

The pictorial convergence that has occurred between man and the apes may be looked upon as involving, on the human side, either a disheartening regression, or a stimulating purification. As the veils of communication have been torn away one by one, leaving today almost naked aestheticism, men have either whistled approvingly, or turned their heads away in disgust, according to the degree to which their individual personalities have leant on traditional elements for support.

In fact, there was no need to whistle *or* turn away. Veils are not even skin deep and a genuine interest in the flesh and blood of aesthetic values can, as already explained, be equally satisfied by either representational or non-representational painting.

Nevertheless it is interesting to see how the veils fell. We have examined what it was that was tearing them off, but what were the step-by-step effects of this process on the pictures themselves?

A rapid survey of painting in the twentieth century gives one the impression that one is looking *backwards* at a superior version of the ontogeny of picture-making by a child. In other words, for 1900 read sixteen years old and for 1960 read two years old. For, as soon as the academic chains

FIG. 52. De-differentiated ambiguity *versus* Un-differentiated ambiguity. Above are examples of de-differentiated representations of the human figure by modern masters (Klee, Miro, Dubuffet),

and here are examples of un-differentiated human figures drawn by young children. Detailed comparisons reveal interesting similarities and differences.

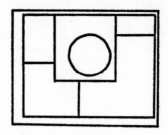

FIG. 53. On this page are geometric-abstract pictures by Nicholson and Mondrian. On the right are pre-representational aggregate patterns by young children. As modern painting has progressed away from the representational, it has unknowingly regressed backwards through the various phases of the child's graphic differentiation.

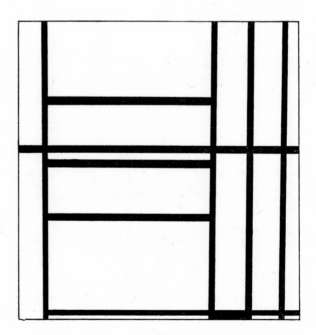

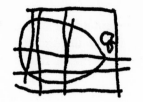

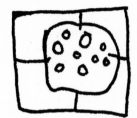

had been broken, the stripping away of the representational and religious elements in painting, through all the various 'isms', ending up today with 'tachism', led back more and more to a concentration on fundamental visual values.

Just as the childlike personages of the pictures of Paul Klee or Joan Miro resemble the early pictorial stages by four- to five-year-old children (see Fig. 52), so the geometric abstractions of Ben Nicholson and Piet Mondrian are reminiscent of the earlier aggregate or combine stages of the three-year-old child (see Fig. 53) and the more 'organic' abstractions of the tachists remind one of the scribble stages of the two-year-old child (see Plates 37 and 38) (or, even more, the ape pictures, owing to the fact that the apes and the tachists share a more advanced muscle control).

I have been especially careful to use such words as 'reminiscent' when comparing these two sets of pictures because there is, of course, a great deal of subtle distinction between them at each stage, the differences being largely a matter of detailed quality and control, rather than basic content.

The progression farther and farther away from the academic schools of representation has now apparently reached its limit. The drift so far has been at base a reaction against something rather than a moving towards something. For the picture-maker today has only his own personal integrity to guide him and he must settle for whatever fits in with his own personal rules. The basic laws of aesthetics can be obeyed at any one of the various points between the two extremes of scribble-like tachism and precise representational realism. It is up to the individual to choose and it is interesting that the various leaders who have pioneered the different art movements of the twentieth century have seldom passed through to later stages. The latter have usually been born of new rebels and new talents. Each painter has found his personal idiom and rested there. A new exhibition of pictures at the present time may offer the visitor anything from emotionally distorted representationalism to cold abstract pattern studies. It is as if new doors have opened rather than that old ones have shut. Now that the picture-maker is no longer forced to serve any one dominant function with his pictures, he can pick and choose according to the dictates of his own temperament. The result is a bewildering but richly varied range of styles and subjects. This has given rise to an upheaval in the world of art teaching. What possible standards can be offered to the art student of today? In many cases the answer has been to ignore the new situation completely and to provide a training of the type that is almost indistinguishable from that of the earlier academies. It is then up to the 'trained' student to fight his own way back from the fully representational to his own personal resting-point somewhere along the scale of de-differentiation.

But many art teachers now feel that the young student should straight away, at the very beginning of his career, be thrust right back to the starting-point of the whole process of differentiation and should begin all over again to develop through the earliest abstract phases. He will now be doing so with the advantages of full muscular control and also with the discipline of an adult mentality. One such teacher, Alan Davie, finds that this is not a very easy process for the art pupil. In a recent document connected with new art teaching methods, called, aptly enough, 'The Developing Process', he has the following statements to make:

> ... I work with the conviction that Art is something basically natural to man. ... It is difficult to rid oneself of false concepts of Art based upon knowledge and cleverness. . . . One must learn to have faith in the intuition which 'knows' without knowledge. . . . To demonstrate the dynamic nature of the creative force, I usually begin with simple exercises in pure idea-less activity: direct putting down of black marks, with no end in view, purposeless and aimless. Strangely enough the student finds that to work without thought requires a great deal of mental discipline, and it is some time before he can achieve an image without the intermediacy of reasoning. . . . The next stage entails the introduction of idea; but idea must also be intuitive, without preliminary discrimination or attachment. . . . Having achieved, after a massive pile of work, through various exercises on many mediums, a faith in the magical inner creative force, the student can enter his own chosen field of creativity, confident in his new-formed freedom. . . .

As Davie suggests, the student who goes through this process is led gradually up a path of *adult* differentiation during his training. He will, of course, go through all the usual exercises including detailed representational drawing, but the latter will now be seen in its correct relationship with other forms of expression, with each as alternative methods, rather than with the one as the inevitable ultimate goal. In the ideal training technique, every form of picture-making should be presented as an alternative of equal validity and importance, so that the young artist is forced to make his own final selection.

It can only be hoped that these and various other new and more personal teaching methods will better equip young painters to face a world in which the functions of picture-making have changed so radically and so rapidly.

The Biological Principles of Picture-making

Any attempt to set out complex and detailed aesthetic rules and regulations is doomed to failure. The history of art theory testifies all too readily to this. The reason is that the basic all-embracing rules are so few and so simple that they would hardly satisfy an art historian. There appear to be only six principles which apply to picture-making as a whole and cover everything and everyone from Leonardo to Congo. They are as follows:

1. The principle of Self-rewarding Activation.
2. The principle of Compositional Control.
3. The principle of Calligraphic Differentiation.
4. The principle of Thematic Variation.
5. The principle of Optimum Heterogeneity.
6. The principle of Universal Imagery.

1. *Self-rewarding Activation.* All pictures, whether by young apes or adult humans, must have a self-rewarding element involved as all or part of the motivation of the picture-maker. Other sociological or materialistic motives may or may not be operating at the same time, but if the production of the picture is not also a reward in itself, then its aesthetic value will be impaired. This particular point has been discussed frequently, but judging by the fact that it is so clearly illustrated by the apes, it would appear basic enough.

In order to test this point, a chimpanzee was once subjected to bribery with a food reward to encourage it to draw more intensely. The outcome of this experiment was most revealing. The ape quickly learnt to associate drawing with getting the reward but as soon as this condition had been established the animal took less and less interest in the lines it was drawing. Any old scribble would do and then it would immediately hold out its hand for the reward. The careful attention the animal had paid previously to design, rhythm, balance and composition was gone and the worst kind of commercial art was born!

2. *Compositional Control.* The evidence obtained from the tests with Alpha, Congo and others shows with great force the powerful and fundamental nature of this principle. It applies throughout picture-making and the simple rules of filling a space, keeping within a space, balancing, and rhythmic repetition, have been dealt with at such length in Chapter 3 that no further elaboration will be made here.

It has been noted that increase in interest in the details of the lines, shapes, or objects that go to make up the composition of a picture may interfere with the compositional control. This happens in young children but it is not unavoidable and the two interests, in composition and calligraphy, can be balanced perfectly in a well-made picture.

It is striking that even in a small capuchin monkey there is a sense of rhythm and balance (see Plate 8). Professor Rensch, who is responsible for this discovery, has also probed deeper into the compositional responses of other species. His findings are briefly as follows:

Using two species of monkey (*Cebus*, a capuchin, and *Ceropithecus*, a guenon) and two species of bird (jackdaw and crow), he carried out a series of preference tests. In each test the animal was presented with a set of white cards on which there were black markings. In any one test, half the cards were marked with a regular, rhythmic pattern and the other half had similar but irregular markings. The individuals of the four species used were all inquisitive creatures and, when confronted with the cards, soon began to investigate the situation by picking one up. Each time this happened, the first choice in a test was noted as either a regular or an irregular card. After hundreds of tests had been performed, statistially significant results were obtained revealing that all four species responded more frequently to the regular patterns rather than the irregular ones.

PREFERENCE TEST PATTERNS	CAPUCHIN MONKEY	GUENON MONKEY	JACKDAW	CROW
1 	+	+	+	=
2 	+	=	+	+
3 	+	+	=	+
4 	+	=	+	+
5 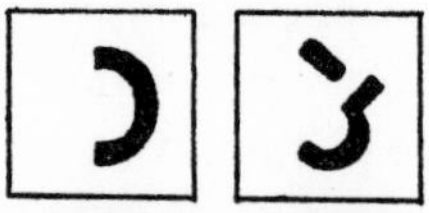	+	+	+	+
6 	+	=	+	+
7 	+	+	−	=
8 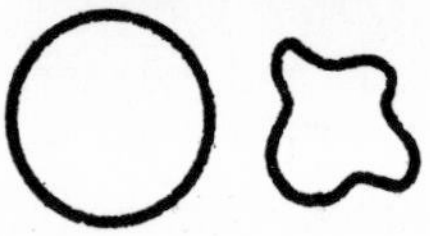	+	+	+	+

FIG. 54. The results of one of Rensch's experiments to test various species for their aesthetic preferences. A + indicates a statistically significant preference for the more regular of the pair of patterns presented. (*After Rensch, 1958*)

The table in Fig. 54 shows the detailed results. Eight of the regular-irregular pairs are illustrated and the results are shown for each species, with a + for a preference for the regular and a — for the irregular. An = sign indicates that there was a fifty-fifty choice and no preference either way. It is interesting that it was the capuchin monkey that showed the highest 'regularity score', with eight out of eight, and that it was this monkey that also made the rhythmic fan-pattern drawing. Rensch has the following to say about the results he obtained:

When choosing between different black patterns on white cardboards the monkeys preferred geometrical, i.e. more regular patterns, to irregular ones. It is very probable that the steadiness of the course of a line, the radial or bilateral symmetry and the repetition of equal components in a pattern (rhythm) were decisive for the preference. (1957) . . . Both species of birds preferred the more regular, more symmetrical or rhythmical patterns. In most cases the percentage of preference was statistically significant. Probably this preference is caused by the better 'complexibility'. i.e. the easier comprehensibility of symmetrical and rhythmical repetitions of the same components ('Rekurrenzlust'). (1958.)

The vital words here are: steadiness – symmetry – repetition – rhythm. These are the basic factors that appeal to the eye and that also appear when, instead of merely selecting ready-made patterns, they are actually being created. There is, so to speak, a positive reaction to order rather than chaos, to organization rather than confusion.

This applies also in the case of the next principle, at the different level of the markings themselves as units rather than the relationships between them. (Indeed, pair No. 8 in the Rensch table is, strictly speaking, more applicable there than here.)

3. *Calligraphic Differentiation.* It is worth repeating that the term 'calligraphic' is being used here in its broadest sense, in relation to all aspects of the nature and details of the component units of a picture, as opposed to the inter-relations of these units.

The important over-riding factor governing this principle is that the development of marks and lines into distinct shapes, in both children and apes, is a slow process of pictorial growth, rather than a series of sudden jumps. This gradual step-by-step development can best be described as a process of differentiation (see Fig. 39) and appears to be a natural process of a very basic type.

In a more sophisticated form, it may be observed amongst adult human painters as well, where it will form an integral part of the modification of old and the evolution of new images and styles. In this last respect it is intimately related to the next principle.

4. *Thematic Variation.* When Congo was given a piece of gymnastic apparatus and allowed to play with it, he would first make erratic exploratory actions and then, out of this confusion, would come a pattern of movement. This he would repeat over and over again until, after a while, he would vary it slightly. Then the variation would grow and grow until the first rhythm was completely lost and a new one replaced it. After a while, another such change would take place and another new pattern would emerge.

There are two factors involved here: the finding of a theme and the subsequent variation of it. Sometimes the basic theme would itself be completely replaced, but more often he would simply find some way of making a slight enough change to produce a variation without completely obscuring the original theme on which it was based.

This process of 'restricted variations on a basic theme' appeared also, as we have seen in Chapters 3 and 4, in his picture-making development. It also figures prominently in all human art, both juvenile and adult. Just as Congo settled for a basic theme (the fan pattern, for instance) and then rang the changes through a number of variations (split fan, centrally-spotted fan, curved fan, reversed fan, etc.) (see Fig. 55) without losing sight of the basic motif, so will a human artist use a similar progression as part of his basic method of working.

Some painters continue throughout their adult painting life with only one theme, which they vary time after time. It is more usual, however, for a painter to progress from theme to theme, each time exhausting a wide range of variations. Progression of this kind is of course involved also in the

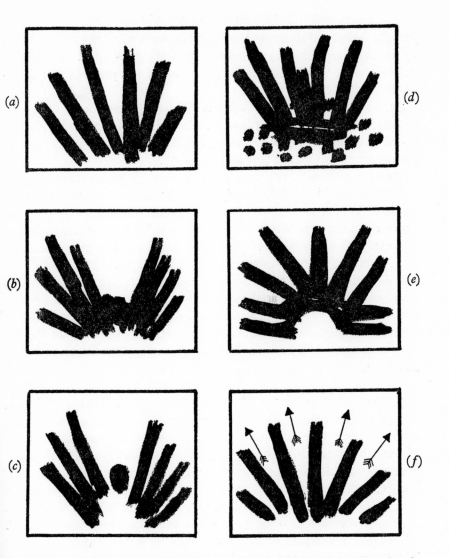

FIG. 55. A diagrammatic representation of the thematic variation in the picture-making of the chimpanzee Congo. (*a*) Simple fan pattern. (*b*) Split fan. (*c*) Centrally-spotted fan. (*d*) Stippled fan-bundle. (*e*) Curved fan. (*f*) Reversed fan.

163

juvenile period and the replacement and exploration of theme after theme by children is intimately associated with the last-named principle of differentiation, where each theme grows out of the previous one in increasing complexity.

At the adult stage, the situation is different. There cannot always be change towards greater complication. Often, a complex phase will be followed by a simple one, as a reaction, and then a further complex one will emerge again, as a second reaction, and so on.

On a less personal level, this process of thematic variation accounts for the succession of 'schools', 'isms', 'vogues', 'fashions' and 'styles' of art, which follow one another at irregular intervals. There is pleasure in the familiar and the repetitive, while the theme is 'on' and minor variations and explorations are active. Then there is the excitement in the novel and unfamiliar, when the theme is changed, and so on.

It is particularly significant that Rensch, in his tests with monkeys, found that when certain aesthetic preference tests were repeated after an interval of time, there was in some cases a statistically significant change in the response. Rensch stressed that this proves the existence in his animals of what he termed 'ästhetische Moden'. Even a monkey, it seems, can be à la mode.

5. *Optimum Heterogeneity.* From the moment work starts on a picture, it begins to shift slowly along a scale from extreme homogeneity (blank space) towards ever-increasing heterogeneity. Maximum heterogeneity (a mass of fussy detail) is not apparently visually desirable and so somewhere along this homogeneous-heterogeneous scale there is, for each picture, a point of Optimum Heterogeneity. This is the point at which the picture is considered to be finished. One mark or line less and it would have been 'incomplete' – one more and it would have been 'overworked'.

This phenomenon might have been predicted as rather specialized, but it is clearly as basic as the four principles listed already, for the occurrence of 'completion' is observed even at the ape level. In tests with Congo it was repeatedly clear that he had a very distinct concept of when a drawing or painting was finished. On the rare occasions when attempts were made

164

o encourage him to continue working on a picture that he considered finished', rather than on a new one, he lost his temper, whimpered, creamed or, if actually persuaded to go on, proceeded to wreck the picture with meaningless or obliterative lines.

There were stages, it must be admitted, when this response to an optimum, rather than a maximum heterogeneity, was eclipsed temporarily and a similar state of affairs applies to children's picture-making. There, the multiple-scribble stage leads often to overall 'blot-out', but this soon metamorphoses into a more organized phase, with the optimum principle operating fully. It is, in fact, remarkable how the pictures made by, say, a five-year-old child, will be exactly right as far as completeness is concerned, with never a line too few, or too many.

It is interesting that no basic overall rule can be laid down concerning the use of colour in picture-making. The infra-human rule appears to be to use as great a variety of colours as possible with a *maximum* heterogeneity rather than an optimum, but this rule does not apply to human painting, at least in historic times. In prehistoric and truly primitive picture-making, the artists may well have used as many colours as they had available to them with their limited technical resources, so that they, like the apes, may well have worked on the principle of as much colour variety as possible. But the colour-variety-rule cannot be stated as a basic principle as colour restrictions of many kinds have been applied in the various epochs of historic times. Exactly why this restraint should have been enforced is not clear at the present.

6. *Universal Imagery.* Much of the imagery of art is universal, both in occurrence and appeal, and, just as certain characteristic arrangements crop up independently with a number of different apes, giving ape pictures as a whole a recognizable character, so, amongst human infants we can see the growth of basic imagery that is universal in its significance and its form of presentation.

The treatment of the human figure has already been described (Fig. 9) and illustrates this perfectly. Another example is given here (Fig. 56) with the house as the basic image. Looking at the five houses shown here

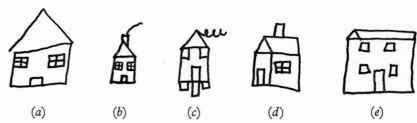

(a)   (b)   (c)   (d)   (e)

FIG. 56. An example of universal imagery. Houses drawn by children from five different countries (a) Denmark. (b) France. (c) India. (d) Finland. (e) Germany. (*After Kellogg, 1955*.)

it is impossible to guess which one stems from which country, so universal is their form. Child art as a whole is startlingly uniform in its imagery and appearance, as are the drawings of *untrained* adults when they are uninhibited enough to make simple pictures. This happens rarely but there are a few regions in which there is extremely rich material available and untapped from the point of view of scientific analysis.

Consider, for example, the universality and uniformity of the images found in the wall drawings in public lavatories, in the pictures of old people in so-called Sunday Painting, and in doodles. Here, with inhibitions removed, the untrained adult reveals that it is not only child art that has a universal imagery.

There seem to be three inter-related factors underlying this universality phenomenon in art. Firstly, there is the *muscular factor*: certain movements of the arm and hand are pleasing and motorically gratifying, whilst others are awkward and difficult to make. As muscular control develops, the influence of this factor will dwindle. This happens especially in professional adult human picture-makers, but less in the other three groups, the apes, the human infants and the 'naïve', or untrained human adults.

Secondly, there is the *optical factor*: certain visual arrangements and impressions are more acceptable to the optical apparatus than others. The famous case of the Golden Number (1.618), for example, has been carefully tested and found to operate with the majority of people. One experiment used is simply to offer to a large number of people a series of white rectangular cards, on a dark surface, with the cards varying in proportion

CONCLUSION – THE BIOLOGY OF ART

from a perfect square to a long thin rectangle. Somewhere in the series
is a card with the Golden Proportions (1:1.618) and it is this card that
the majority of people will select when asked to pick out the most beautiful one in the series (see Fig. 57).

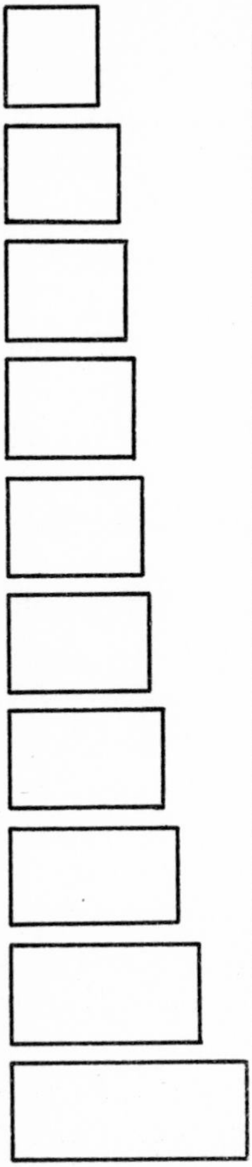

$\frac{1}{1}$	3%
$\frac{5}{6}$	0%
$\frac{4}{5}$	1%
$\frac{3}{4}$	3%
$\frac{20}{29}$	9%
$\frac{2}{3}$	20%
$\frac{21}{34}$	35%
$\frac{13}{23}$	19%
$\frac{1}{2}$	8%
$\frac{2}{5}$	2%

The explanation of the Golden Number is that it is related to the spacing of our eyes and the range of our visual field and it has been suggested that a man, one-eyed from birth, should prefer squares, on this same principle.

This and other optical influences will guide the path of picture development very intensely prior to the creation of the earliest representational images and will determine their early forms. But, as the child grows and the differentiation process advances, so the optical factor will take second place, along with the muscular factor, as the third basic influence, the *psychological factor*, increases steadily.

As soon as the child has portrayed a specific person or a specific place, there will be strong psychological undercurrents controlling the exact way in which it is presented in the picture. As there are much greater individual differences in personal psychology than in arm musculature, or

FIG. 57. The Golden Mean Test. When shown the ten shapes drawn here and asked which is the most pleasing, the majority chose the one with the so-called 'Golden Proportions' (1:1.618). The left-hand column indicates the proportions of each shape and the right-hand column shows the percentage preferences. (*Based on data from Borissavlievitch, 1958.*)

167

optical structure, it is not surprising that it is amongst the professional adult human picture-maker, where the muscular and optical factors are most completely suppressed by the intellect, that one gets the greatest pictorial variation and the weakest universality of imagery. In the pictures of young children, or untrained adults, the universality is greater, owing to the levelling effect of the muscular limitations and also the (as yet unobliterated) legacy of the strong pre-representational domination by optical influences over the image precursors.

Future Studies

These six points may be termed the biological principles of picture-making and have been selected because they appear to govern the picture-making of both man and the apes. Any rules that are basic enough to apply to several related species, rather than to one species or (as is more often the case in art theory) to one epoch of one species, must indeed be fundamental to the activity concerned.

Only by further comparative studies, with many individuals of different species tested under identical conditions, will it be possible to elaborate further on the six principles stated here, or to add new principles to the list. This is the task for the future and it can only be hoped that one day we shall witness the establishment of an Institute for the Study of the Biology of Art. At such an institute, using carefully selected teams of apes and monkeys, there is little doubt that a great deal more of the mystery of the process of artistic creation could be unravelled. With comparable tests applied to human infants and also to other specialized groups from a variety of human cultures, much more firmly established comparative data would rapidly be forthcoming.

The work so far has been, for the most part, fragmentary and uncoordinated but it is hoped that it, and this book, have served to whet the appetite and encourage an interest in the further development of what is still virtually a new field of study.

Literature

ALSCHULER, R. H. and L. B. W. HATTWICK (1947). *Painting and Personality.* A study of young children. 2 Vols. University of Chicago Press, Chicago.

ARCHER, W. G. and ROBERT MELVILLE (1949). *40,000 Years of Modern Art.* Institute of Contemporary Arts, London.

ARNHEIM, RUDOLPH (1956). *Art and Visual Perception.* Faber & Faber, London.

BORISSAVLIEVITCH, M. (1958). *The Golden Number.* Tiranti, London.

BRODERICK, A. H. (1948). *Prehistoric Painting.* Avalon Press, London.

DAVIDSON, D. S. (1936). *Aboriginal Australian and Tasmanian Rock Carvings and Paintings.* Memoirs of the American Philosophical Society, Vol. 5. Philadelphia.

ENG, HELGA (1931). *The Psychology of Children's Drawings.* Routledge & Kegan Paul, London.

GOJA, H. (1959). *Zeichen Versuche mit Menschenaffen.* Zeitschrift für Tierpsychologie, Vol. 16, pp. 369–73.

GOODENOUGH, F. L. (1926). *Measurement of Intelligence by Drawings.* World Book Company, New York.

GROZINGER, W. (1955). *Scribbling, Drawing, Painting.* The early forms of the child's pictorial creativeness. Faber & Faber, London.

HEDIGER, H. (1953). *Operative Fremdkörper – Entfernung aus dem Magen eines Gorillas.* Zoologische Garten, Vol. 20, pp. 89–95.

HESS, LILO (1954). *Christine the Baby Chimp.* Bell, London.

HOGBEN, LANCELOT (1949). *From Cave Painting to Comic Strip.* Max Parrish, London.

KELLOGG, RHODA (1955). *What Children Scribble and Why.* Author's edition, San Francisco.

KELLOGG, W. N. and L. A. KELLOGG (1933). *The Ape and the Child.* McGraw-Hill, New York.

KLEE, PAUL (1925). *Pädagogisches Skizzenbuch.* Bauhaus, Weimar. (Later published in English as the *Pedagogical Sketchbook* by Faber & Faber, London.)

KLEE, PAUL (1945). *Uber die moderne Kunst.* Benteli Bern-Bumpliz. (Published in English in 1948 as *On Modern Art* by Faber & Faber, London.)

169

LITERATURE

KLUVER, H. (1933). *Behaviour Mechanisms in Monkeys*. Chicago.

KOCH, RUDOLPH (1930). *The Book of Signs*. First Edition Club, London. (Later published in U.S.A. by Dover Publications.)

KOHLER, W. (1925). *The Mentality of Apes*. Harcourt Brace, New York.

KOHTS, N. (1935). *Infant Ape and Human Child*. Scientific Memoirs of the Museum Darwinianum, Moscow.

KOHTS, N. (1958). *The Development of the Mind in the Evolutionary Process of Organisms*. Moscow.

KORTLANDT, A. (1959). *Tussen Mens en Dier*. Wolters, Groningen.

LEVY, MERVYN (1958). *The Lost Image*. Exhibition Catalogue, London.

LIMBOUR, GEORGES (1958). *Jean Dubuffet*. Exhibition Catalogue. Arthur Tooth, London.

MACHOVER, K. (1949). *Personality Projection in the drawing of the Human Figure*. Thomas, Springfield.

MORRIS, DESMOND (1957). *Paintings by Chimpanzees*. Exhibition Catalogue. Institute of Contemporary Arts, London.

MORRIS, DESMOND (1958). *The Behaviour of Higher Primates in Captivity*. XVth International Congress of Zoology, London.

MORRIS, DESMOND (1958). *The Story of Congo*. Batsford, London.

MORRIS, DESMOND (1958). *Paintings by Congo*. Lost Image Exhibition Catalogue, London.

MORRIS, DESMOND (1958). *Pictures by Chimpanzees*. New Scientist, Vol. 4, pp. 609–11.

MORRIS, DESMOND (1959). *Schimpansen-Kunst*. Sie und Er, Vol. 35, pp. 18–19.

MORRIS, DESMOND (1961). *Primates aesthetics*. Natural History, Vol. 70, pp. 22–29.

NAVRATIL, L. (1958). *The figure drawing test*. Triangle, Vol. 3, pp. 317–25.

OAKLEY, K. P. (1950). *Man the Toolmaker*. British Museum, London.

PASMORE, VICTOR, et al. (1959). *The Developing Process*. University of Durham.

PENROSE, ROLAND (1958). *Language of the Wall, Parisian Graffiti*. Exhibition Catalogue. Institute of Contemporary Arts, London.

RENSCH, B. (1957). *Asthetische Faktoren bei Farb– und Formbevorzugungen von Affen*. Zeitschrift für Tierpsychologie, Vol. 14, pp. 71–99.

RENSCH, B. (1958). *Die Wirksamkeit asthetischer Faktoren bei Wirbeltieren*. Zeitschrift für Tierpsychologie, Vol. 15, pp. 447–61.

LITERATURE

SCHILLER, P. (1951). *Figural preferences in the drawings of a Chimpanzee.* Journal of Comparative and Physiological Psychology, Vol. 44, pp. 101–11.

SOKOLOWSKY, A. (1928). *Erlebnisse mit wilden Tieren.* Haberland, Liepzig.

YERKES, R. M. (1943). *Chimpanzees, a Laboratory Colony.* Yale University Press, New Haven.

Acknowledgements

Many people have helped with this study, in various ways, and I would particularly like to acknowledge the assistance of the following: James Bomford, for arousing my interest in art theory in the first place; Sir Solly Zuckerman, Dr L. Harrison Matthews and Sidney Bernstein, for making the major study with Congo possible; Donald Harker, Mrs Dorothy Moreland, Arthur Watson, and Mervyn Levy, for the parts they played in organizing the exhibitions of ape pictures; Sir Julian Huxley, Sir Herbert Read, Dr Konrad Lorenz, Dr Fae Hall, and Dr W. M. S. Russell, for valuable discussions; Professor Bernhard Rensch, Professor Heini Hediger, Dr Antoni Kortlandt, Dr A. C. V. van Bemmel, Dr Hermann Goja, Madam N. Kohts, Mrs Crane Chadbourne, Tony Fitzgerald, Michael Lyster, and Chris Baris, for information about, material from, or assistance with the various primates; Lady Zuckerman, Dr E. Oakshot, Mrs Simon Hughes-Stanton, Mrs Rhoda Kellogg, and Paul Vaughan, for similar valuable help in connexion with children's pictures. Finally, I would like to thank my wife, Ramona, for her help and encouragement throughout all the phases of this study.

Acknowledgements are due to the following for permission to reproduce some of the illustrations in this book: Michael Lyster for Plates 18 and 20–26; Planet News Ltd for Plates 17 and 27; Camera Press Ltd for Plates 7 and 9; and Keystone Press Agency Ltd for Plate 5.

Index

Abreu, Mrs Rosalia, 15, 16
Achilla, 28, 29, 43, 48
action paintings, 34
aesthetic vogues, 33, 164
aggregates, 116, 117, 122
Alexander, 28, 29, 43, 57, 104; *Plates*
  A, B
Alpha, 18, 20, 21, 30, 31, 43, 45–51,
  59–66, 69, 73, 90, 92, 93, 102, 103,
  113, 121, 134, 139–41, 159
Alschuler, 26
Altamira, 143
ambiguous figures, 64
Amsterdam Zoo, 31, 33, 44
Asia, 147
Australia, 147

balancing of figures, 62, 63, 65, 80–87,
  102, 103, 106, 108, 111, 112, 141
Baltimore Zoo, 24, 25, 27, 43
Baris, Chris, 28, 29, 43; *Plates 7, 9*
Basle Zoo, 28, 43
bed-making, 95–97
Beebee, 36, 38, 39, 44, 111
Bella, 30–33, 38, 39, 44, 69, 101
Betsy, 24–28, 43, 58; *Plates 2, 3, 4*
Beth, 24, 25
Borissavlievitch, 167

Canary Islands, 15, 18
capuchin monkey, 18, 30, 32, 34, 40,
  43, 44, 48, 69, 96, 97, 101, 141,
  159–61; *Plates 8, 14–16*
Cebus, 159

'cephaloped', 124, 126
Cercopithecus, 159
Charlie, 36, 39, 44, 110–12
Chimpanzee, 13–103, 109–15, 127–48,
  158, 159, 162–5
Christine, 24, 39, 43
cinematography, 159
circle, 31, 117–25, 132, 133, 135, 142
Clare, 40, 44; *Plates 14, 15*
Cobra, 4, 44; *Plate 16*
colour choice, 54; *Plate 17*
combines, 116, 117, 122
completion of figures, 63, 65, 89, 90,
  102, 103, 108
Congo, 21–23, 26–30, 32–35, 38, 39,
  43, 45, 48–58, 65–103, 108, 109,
  113–15, 118, 124, 127–41, 158,
  159, 162–4; *Plates 5, 6, 17–36;*
  C-M
copying, 126
corner-marking, 30, 41, 59, 60, 62, 65,
  90–93, 102, 121
crow, 33, 159–61
Cuba, 15, 16

dancing, 145
Davie, Alan, 157
Denmark, 122, 166
diagonal cross, 118, 121, 122, 138
diagrams, 116–18, 121, 122, 134–8, 142
Dr Tom, 24, 25, 43
dog, 117
doodles, 166
Dubuffet, 152

173